HOW TO
READ
THE SCIENCES

507
Ad19h

22,634

W. Royce Adams, *Santa Barbara City College*

Science Consultant

Paul DeHart Hurd, *Stanford University*

Scott, Foresman and Company

Developed by Educational Development Corporation 1970

Modern Technical Physics by Arthur Beiser (Reading, Mass.: Addison-Wesley Publishing Co., Inc., 1966). Used by permission of the publisher.

The Physical Sciences: From Atoms to Stars, Second Edition, by Theodore A. Ashford (New York: Holt, Rinehart and Winston, Inc., 1967). Used by permission of the publisher.

Botany: Principles and Problems, 6th edition, by Edmund W. Sinnott and Katherine S. Wilson (New York: McGraw-Hill Book Company, 1963). Used by permission of the publisher.

The Science of Zoology by Paul B. Weisz (New York: McGraw-Hill Book Company, 1966). Used by permission of the publisher.

Physical Geology, Third Edition, by L. Don Leet and Sheldon Judson (Englewood Cliffs, N.J.: Prentice-Hall, Inc., 1965). Used by permission of the publisher.

College Chemistry by Leo H. Spinar (Glenview, Ill.: Scott, Foresman and Company, 1968). Used by permission of the publisher.

The Cellular Role of Macromolecules by P. H. Jellinck (Glenview, Ill.: Scott, Foresman and Company, 1967). Used by permission of the publisher.

Table of Contents

PREFACE

The threefold increase in college enrollments since mid-century has brought with it many students who are deficient in the skills needed to do college level work. A major deficiency is how to read the materials of subjects that make up their program of study. The emphasis in learning science upon the attainment of concepts and principles and upon knowing their precise meaning demands a special kind of reading unfamiliar to many students.

How to Read the Sciences provides insights and practice in the reading of sciences typically encountered by students in the first year of college. The students are alerted to the learning requirements of the subject and then shown how to read in these terms. Special exercises are provided to acquaint students with the vocabulary demands of science and how this knowledge is related to comprehension and meaning.

The effective learning of science requires that whatever is read and studied be organized in some meaningful way through notes or outlines. Successful retention is based on understanding what is read and building a valid synthesis of ideas. Since college students are expected to be self-directed learners, the need for reading capabilities is evident; *How to Read the Sciences* provides the means for developing the specialized skills needed for studying science.

Paul DeHart Hurd
Science Consultant
Stanford University

FOREWORD: TO THE INSTRUCTOR

Efficient reading requires flexibility: the ability to adapt one's reading style to the nature of the material and to one's purpose in reading it. Readers who have this ability can vary their reading style from book to book and even from page to page. For those who don't, there is only one way to read, whether they are reading a newspaper, a legal document, a novel, or a textbook.

For the beginning college student who lacks reading flexibility, the going may be rough. He is confronted suddenly with a reading load that can exceed by far anything he has ever experienced. If he continues to approach everything with a single reading style, he is likely to find himself hopelessly behind in his assignments, no matter how much diligence he can muster. This is a serious problem. It affects the performance of a great many students.

This book—like its two companion volumes, *How to Read the Social Sciences* and *How to Read the Humanities*—helps the college student learn how to make the necessary reading-style adjustments. It introduces him to the four steps that are basic to good reading habits—Exploring; Checking the Vocabulary; Analyzing for Comprehension; Synthesizing for Understanding. As each step is explained, it is applied to examples taken from current textbooks.

By examining the forms and patterns of writing peculiar to each major subject area and understanding the differences, the student can develop his ability to sense what reading style is appropriate to a particular assignment. He learns, in addition, several ways to expand and structure his understanding of what he reads.

Most important of all, perhaps, he is encouraged (with examples) to relate to what he reads in a personal way.

INTRODUCTION: TO THE STUDENT

Why this book concentrates on reading science

Why a whole book on how to read the sciences? Perhaps that can best be answered with an illustration. The following two passages are taken from a science text. Before reading the passages, find a watch or clock with a second hand so that you can time your reading of each passage. Write down your beginning time and your finishing time. Do this separately for each passage.

Beginning time: _____
Begin reading.

▶ ## Properties

We recognize the various forms of matter by their properties and we distinguish them from one another by the differences in their properties. By *properties* of materials we simply mean the way they affect our senses or our instruments, and also by their behavior under certain conditions or toward other materials. Thus, we recognize charcoal by its black color and its ability to burn in air; sugar by its white color, its sweetness, and its solubility in water. We distinguish aluminum from iron by its lightness, its low strength to bending forces, and its resistance to rusting. For these reasons these properties are called *characteristic properties*.

Properties are usually classified as *physical*, *chemical*, and *physiological*. Among the physical properties are color, density, solubility in water or in other media, melting point, boiling point, hardness, electrical conductivity, and many others. Chemical properties are such behavior as ability to burn in air, to char on heating, and in general to react (or *fail* to react) with other substances. Physiological properties are such properties as odor, taste, ability to act as a medicinal or a poison. The exact classification is not too important, at present, except to bring out the significant point that many and diverse properties may be used to identify a kind of matter and to distinguish it from all other kinds. Many of the properties can be measured with high precision. Each kind of material has but one set of properties. It differs from all other kinds in at least one property.[1] ◀

---

[1]From *The Physical Sciences: From Atoms to Stars*, Second Edition, by Theodore A. Ashford. Copyright © 1960, 1967 by Holt, Rinehart and Winston, Inc. Reprinted by permission of Holt, Rinehart and Winston, Inc.

Stop reading and check the time.
Finishing time: _____

Do the same thing with the following passage. Write down both your beginning time and your finishing time.

Beginning time: _____
Begin reading.

► *Density*. We shall single out *density* as an example of a property and define it more precisely. Density is a measure of "lightness" or "heaviness" of materials. It is a measure of the compactness of matter. More precisely, density is the amount of matter per unit volume, that is,

$$\text{density} = \frac{\text{mass}}{\text{volume}}$$

or in symbols

$$D = \frac{m}{V}$$

Density can be measured with high precision. Thus, the density of the "light" aluminum is 2.702 grams per cubic centimeter, and that of the "heavy" lead is 11.3437 grams per cubic centimeter. The densities of water, ice, iron, mercury, and gold are 1.000, 0.9168, 7.12, 13.5951, and 19.3 grams per cubic centimeter, respectively. Liquids and solids range in density from a fraction of a gram per *cubic centimeter* for such substances as cork, to 22.48 grams per *cubic centimeter* for osmium, the densest substance known. Gases, on the other hand, are about 1000 times lighter under ordinary conditions—their densities being of the order of a few grams per 1000 cubic centimeters. Each substance has its own precise density. The same thing is true of the other properties.[2] ◄

Stop reading and check the time.
Finishing time: _____

Now compare the time it took you to read each passage. The two passages are almost equal in length. Are your reading times almost equal? They may be, but chances are, it took you longer to read the second selection even though it is shorter. The concepts in the second selection are more complex and require more mental agility. Comprehension, not speed, is important here.

---

[2] *Ibid.*, pp. 182–183.

Try the following questions based on the selections you just read. Do not refer back to the passages. Answer only from what you remember reading.

1. We recognize the various forms of matter by their
   a. differences.
   b. properties.
   c. density.
2. By properties of materials, we mean
   a. the way materials affect our senses or our instruments.
   b. the material's behavior under certain conditions.
   c. both *a* and *b*.
3. Which one of the following is not a classification of properties?
   a. physical   c. physiological
   b. chemical   d. anatomical
4. True or False: Many of the properties of materials can be measured with high precision.
5. True or False: Each kind of material has only one set of properties.
6. Density is defined as
   a. an example of a property of materials.
   b. a measure of "lightness" or "heaviness" of materials.
   c. a characteristic property.
7. The symbols $D = m/V$ represent: D_____
                                    m_____
                                    V_____
8. Which of the following has the greatest density?
   a. aluminum   c. iron
   b. lead   d. gold
9. Which of the following is the densest substance known?
   a. cork   c. osmium
   b. mercury   d. gases
10. Liquids and solids range in density from a fraction of a gram per cubic centimeter to
    a. 13.5951 grams per cubic centimeter.
    b. 19.3 grams per cubic centimeter.
    c. 22.48 grams per cubic centimeter.
    d. 1000 grams per cubic centimeter.

Compare your answers with these: 1. b; 2. c; 3. d; 4. True; 5. True; 6. b; 7. Density, mass, Volume; 8. d; 9. c; 10. c.

The two passages you read, even though taken from the same book, required different reading skills. The first passage simply provided factual statements defining property and discussing different types of properties. The second passage demands more of a reader because it contains more advanced ideas and terms.

There are, of course, other writing patterns used in science textbooks which require you to classify things, to solve problems, to conduct experiments, and to explain complicated processes. All this means that you must be able to see beyond all the illustrations, examples, and details to get a firm grasp of the major points or ideas being presented. You need reading-analysis skills.

The reading of the two passages should have shown you that you can't read everything at the same rate of speed. Some writing patterns are easier to read and follow, while others must be read slowly and sometimes reread. You need to be able to adjust your reading rate.

The questions you answered on the passages should show you how well you can read both simple and more complex science writing. The first five questions were based on the first passage, the last five on the second. Which questions were the easiest to answer? Usually, when both passages are read at the same speed, the last five questions are more difficult.

You read the passages and answered the questions. You became involved. Without involvement your reading will be superficial and your comprehension of short duration. To understand what you are reading in science, you must become involved in it.

How to Read the Sciences concentrates on reading the sciences only. Science textbooks are not written like other textbooks, and they cannot be read like other textbooks. Each of the different writing patterns used in science textbooks is geared to the type of material being presented. This book will help you learn how to change your reading style to fit each writing pattern. Understanding the patterns of science writing will be easier if you have a clear picture of the differences between science and other fields of knowledge.

What science does

The *humanities* deal with feelings, dispositions, and sympathies of man through the study of literature, music, art, philosophy, and religion.

The *social sciences* look at the "superorganisms" — an entire culture, an entire economy, an entire political system — to find out why they behave as they do, what makes them work, and what makes them break down.

Science is the accumulation of knowledge through study, observation, and classification of facts with the establishment of verifiable general laws or truths.

Scientists seek information about the structures and processes of nature, and this information should not be affected by the feelings or beliefs that keep a culture or a society going.

A scientist's choice of methods, techniques, or equipment will depend on many things, including the nature of the question to be answered, and the resources available. He may use one method or many. He may invent a new method or device for use in his researches. Nevertheless, most scientific inquiry in the past has used one or more of the following processes:

1. observation
2. description
3. classification (taxonomy)
4. experimentation
5. construction of concepts, theories, or analogies that fit the observable data: the "law," the formula, and the model

Theory and experimentation are often interdependent. A good theory stimulates experiments that spawn new theories, and so on.

What science doesn't do

Science does not discover the "laws of nature." Laws, like crime and punishment, are human inventions. Boyle's law, Newton's third law of motion, the first law of thermodynamics are apparently valid man-made statements about nature. Each can be used to predict events in nature or to design machines that work.

Scientific methods and writings

Every human being has feelings, values, attitudes, beliefs, and prejudices. How we see reality is influenced (distorted) by these qualities, but the scientist seeks an undistorted picture of reality.

Suppose a scientist is asking the kind of questions that will have a yes-or-no answer, like the following:

1. Does the earth move around the sun?
2. Is it possible to create a vacuum?
3. Is marijuana addictive?

Each of these factual questions has at one time aroused strong feelings in people, and scientists, after all, are people. It's easy to say you'll just look at the facts, but your way of looking is conditioned by your feelings.

What can the scientist do about his feelings? He can't rid himself of them, nor would he want to. Being aware of his feelings helps, but the most effective tactics are those built into the *experimental design*. In setting up his experiment or study, the scientist uses all of his conscious ingenuity in trying to outwit his unconscious ingenuity. He erects all kinds of barriers and safeguards to prevent his feelings and opinions from influencing the results or his interpretation of the results. If he is successful, other scientists, regardless of their opinions, will be able to repeat the experiment, and their results will agree.

When a scientist writes, the nature of his subject matter dictates a certain pattern. For example, when a scientist describes how mitosis works, his writing pattern will be different from the explanation of how the Cartesian way of looking at the universe differed from the Aristotelian.

Therefore, the scientific writing pattern is determined by the type of information being presented.

Each major subject area has its own peculiar writing patterns. Each requires a particular reading approach and a specialized vocabulary. To illustrate these differences, here are three distinct patterns, all dealing with the subject of fish.

Description 1

Fish Story [3]

Richard Armour

Count this among my heartfelt wishes:
To hear a fish tale told by fishes
And stand among the fish who doubt
The honor of a fellow trout,
And watch the bulging of their eyes
To hear of imitation flies
And worms with rather droopy looks
Stuck through with hateful, horrid hooks,
And fishermen they fled all day from
(As big as this) and got away from.

Description 2

► Fishing

Although the Mesolithic was still a hunting and food-collecting stage, men now learned to hunt new forms of life: In the coastal and lake regions of Europe they constructed semipermanent sites where they hunted along the peripheries and fished intensively along the shores. (Spearing fish seems to have been engaged in during the Upper Paleolithic also.) New kinds of fishhooks were devised, the barbed harpoon was brought to a new level of usage, fish traps and weirs were constructed to catch large quantities of fish, and the process of smoking both fish and meat was evidently also discovered.[4] ◄

[3]"Fish Story" from Light Armour by Richard Armour. Copyright © 1942, 1054, Curtis Publishing Company; © 1954, Richard Armour. Used with permission of McGraw-Hill Book Company.
[4]From An Introduction to Man and His Development by David Rodnick. Copyright © 1966 by Meredith Publishing Company. Reprinted by permission of Appleton-Century-Crofts.

Description 3

▶ For a fish or a swimmer under water, all the world above the surface of the water appears contained in a cone of 98 degrees (Figure I.1). Objects on the horizon appear along the line *OA* or *OB*. Similarly, the light entering the eye is refracted by the lens of the eye, so that we can see "with the corner of our eye" objects directly to our right or left, even though we are looking straight forward. They are of course distorted. In looking straight ahead, how much of the total space can we see?[5] ◀

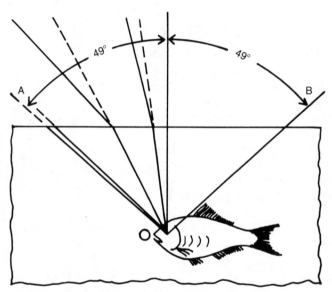

Figure 1.1. The world of a fish, above the surface, is contained in a cone less than 100 degrees.

Description 1 is an example of a writing pattern often found in the humanities: a poem. Although some facts may be contained in the poem, it deals mostly with feelings. Description 2 comes from a social science textbook. The author is concerned with man's historical development in society. Description 3 is from a physics textbook, and it is more factual and precise. Everything stated about the subject of fish is based on observation and measurement. Facts are more important in science than feelings or historical significance.

Different kinds of writing call for different kinds of reading. Each has its own viewpoint, its own vocabulary, its own purpose. The main purpose of this book is to show you the special characteristics of scientific

---

[5]Ashford, *op. cit.*, p. 176.

writing, and the special approach needed in reading and understanding these patterns.

A look at this book

How to Read the Sciences offers four basic steps for reading the sciences. Step One: *Explore* gives you a purpose for reading other than the fact that it was assigned. Exploring helps you concentrate on what you are reading and speeds up your comprehension.

Step Two: *Check the Vocabulary* deals both with the language of science and with methods for developing your own vocabulary. To fully understand what you are reading, you must understand the words used and their purpose.

Step Three: *Analyze for Comprehension* shows you how to get better comprehension from what you are reading — the "close" reading. Examples are taken from actual biology, physics, chemistry, botany, psychology, and zoology textbooks to show you the approaches needed for the six common reading patterns which occur in science textbooks: the classification pattern, the process-description pattern, the factual-statement pattern, the experiment-instructions pattern, the problem-solving pattern, and various combinations of patterns.

Step Four: *Synthesize for Understanding* gives you some practical approaches to taking notes as you read, using outside reading sources, and taking tests. To synthesize is to put pieces together to form a complete pattern. This step helps you put together the other three parts of the reading process.

Although these four steps are treated separately, they work together in the total reading process. The book builds one step upon the other, but you should feel free to turn first to whatever section of the book you feel you need most as long as you understand the basic step itself.

Reading-rate improvement (words read per minute) is not given special treatment in this book. The purpose here is to make you a better reader in the sciences. The use of the four steps as a whole, however, may help you increase your reading rate. You will find occasional exercises in the practice pages of this book which can be timed for a words-per-minute rate check.

All the reading selections used here are taken from textbooks that are actually used in science classes throughout the country. You might check each to see whether it is from your own science textbook. Whenever possible, the book is intended to be practical. The style and tone are straightforward, informal, and easy so that you can get through this one quickly and on to your science textbook.

Take a moment now to study the Table of Contents. That should help you understand better the four basic steps which you have just read about. Then you will be ready for Step One.

W. R. A.

ONE

Explore

Suddenly in the middle of reading your biology assignment it occurs to you that you're not thinking about biology at all. That movie you saw last night has somehow managed to slip back into your thoughts. Retracing the pages you read, you realize that while your eyes have covered five pages, your mind hasn't. In spite of good intentions, you weren't able to devote a solid ten minutes of reading time to your assignments without your mind wandering.

This is a familiar story to many readers, so much so that some have grown to accept loss of concentration as part of the study routine. But it doesn't have to be that way. You can learn to control such aimless mind-wandering and thus speed up your reading and reduce study time. In fact, that's what Step One: *Explore* is all about. The chapters in this section can help you get better reading results if you are willing to follow the advice given.

Your mind may wander away from your reading for many reasons. You may not have a real interest in the subject. You may lack the vocabulary you need to understand what you are reading. You may be too tired, or you may have problems with a girl friend, or worries about a part-time job. Or you may just be unfamiliar with the correct way to approach academic subject matter. Whatever the cause, your mind would be less likely to wander if you had prepared yourself to read.

Step One: *Explore* is the first of four major steps in this book that will help you read the sciences better. Chapters 1 and 2 offer you ways of preparing yourself so that you can read for thorough comprehension. You will learn what it means to explore both your textbook and your chapter assignments. While the examples used are all taken from actual science textbooks, the information about exploring can be used on any reading material. Remember that the information you gain from using this book can only be helpful if you apply it to your assignments.

1

Exploring Your Textbook

The total picture. As you read this chapter, remember that it is only one of two chapters that explain exploring as a step toward better reading. This chapter discusses exploring, how to explore the textbook's basic content and purpose, and how to explore lab manuals. Before reading any further, make certain that you have read the Introduction carefully and that you understand how Step One: *Explore* is only a part of the total study reading process.

Testing this textbook—and you

Try answering these questions without looking up anything:

1. What is the title of this book?

2. Who is the author and what do you know about him?

3. When was this book published?

4. What are the major divisions of this book?

5. Why is this book specifically devoted to how to read the sciences and not to how to read in general?

If you were able to answer all five questions without flipping pages to find the answers, you already know how to explore a textbook. You've tested the textbook, know its purpose, and understand its basic organization. So don't waste your time reading something you already know. Move on to the next section of this chapter. But if you couldn't answer the questions or if you don't see why you should be able to answer them, read on.

Take a moment right now and explore this book by reading

1. the title page (not the cover),
2. the copyright page and the Foreword,
3. the Table of Contents, and
4. the Introduction.

Now you should be able to answer the five questions asked earlier. Try them again.

Having explored this book, you should now know whether it is up to date. The date of printing is especially important when you deal with subjects that change quickly, such as science. You don't want a book that contains out-of-date information. Do you think the copyright date on a book like this is important? Why?

The author of your book is another point to consider when exploring a textbook. The title page tells you where the author teaches. But the Foreword and Introduction tell you his reasons for writing the book and for organizing it as he has. Knowing this can help you understand the author's purpose, which in turn helps you understand the book's intent and direction.

This book is divided into four major sections, each one with its own Preface. The Introduction explains these four sections or steps and discusses how all four are to be used together. It also explains why this book is devoted only to reading the sciences. You also learned that each chapter begins with *The total picture* and ends with a summary. In between, subheadings divide the chapter into smaller sections.

You may be wondering why it's so important to be able to answer such exploring questions. Actually, exploring is just a common-sense approach to reading. You probably wouldn't go out looking for a job without looking in the want-ad columns first. Generally you don't go into a chemistry lab and mix chemicals without having prepared for the lab through lectures, demonstrations, or reading. Preparation comes first. Exploring is preparing to read.

There are many reasons why students have difficulty reading. But one of the biggest problems is lack of preparation. Psychologists claim that we forget about 80 percent of what we read within two weeks unless we approach our reading correctly. Exploring before careful reading helps you know what you can expect in the assignment and push other matters from your mind so you can concentrate. Exploring is also helpful when you are reading a book only because it was assigned and not because you are especially interested in the subject. But a good exploration can often help you create an interest or a purpose that is more meaningful.

Exploring your science textbook

Science covers a wide range of subjects, but one science course most students take is biology. Suppose that you are enrolled in Biology 1. It's the first day of class and the instructor hands out a course outline that looks like this:

BIOLOGY 1 - STUDY GUIDE

This is a course for non-science majors. It will attempt to define the science of biology, examine the principal methods of science investigation, and apply some of the methods of investigation in laboratory situations.

The course will be divided into five basic units:

    Unit 1 -- Cell Life
    Unit 2 -- Evolution
    Unit 3 -- Plants
    Unit 4 -- Animals
    Unit 5 -- Heredity

Grades will be based on the total number of points earned during the semester. The maximum number of points possible is 500, as designated below:

    Mid-term exam   150 points
    Lab quizzes (6--given every
       other Wednesday)   60 points
    Reading reports (6)   60 points
    Regular attendance   30 points
    Final exam   200 points
                                      500 points

Six reading reports are to be turned in during the semester. These reports should be turned in on 5 x 8 cards and should contain complete bibliographical information. The reports should be based on an article found in the following journals:

    American Scientist   Natural History
    Scientific American   Biological Bulletin
    American Zoologist   Nature
    Science   BioScience
    Journal of Mammalogy   Perspectives in Biology and Medicine

The major textbook will be Biology, Its Principles and Implications by Garrett Hardin, 2nd ed., W. H. Freeman and Company, 1966.

A handout sheet such as this actually helps you explore the course. It shows you what you are going to study, how many exams and quizzes you will have, how you will be graded, what reports you will have to do, and what textbook you will use.

Your next step should be to buy the textbook and explore it, even though you may not have been given assignments in it yet. Read the Preface and the Introduction; examine the Table of Contents and compare it to your handout sheet; and look for glossaries or appendixes which might be useful later.

For illustration purposes, here is part of the Preface from the textbook mentioned on the handout sheet. It may be the one you are using in your biology class.

► Preface[1]

With the beginning of the second half of the twentieth century two publications turned biology in new directions. The first of these has frequently been singled out for notice: Watson and Crick's two-page paper, "Molecular structure of nucleic acids," which appeared in 1953. In the complex endeavor we call science it is always somewhat unfair to identify any one contribution as crucial; but if a single publication may be said to have announced the coming of age of molecular biology, it is this one.

In 1962 a contribution of an utterly different sort was made by Rachel Carson, with the publication of her book, *Silent Spring*. Watson and Crick's work dealt with the ultramicroscopic organization of living matter; the scale of Miss Carson's was global. The assertions of the molecular biologists were made with great precision; those of *Silent Spring* were more general, more qualified, and more controversial. Miss Carson's work has been both praised and criticized; but whatever its merits, I think it is clear by now that this impassioned work has redirected the attention of biologists to their civic responsibilities. Every plucking at the web of life produces multiple effects, in which the distinction between "principal effect" and "side effects" is merely a reflection of our desires. It is the function of ecology to furnish an intellectual framework on which may be displayed the consequences of human interference in the world of nature. On rare occasions—much rarer than we would like to think—we can alter natural arrangements in a way that favors the ends of man. The deliberate human interventions that produce some ob-

[1]From *Biology, Its Principles and Implications* by Garrett Hardin (San Francisco: W. H. Freeman and Company, Copyright © 1966), p. v.

vious good effects (amply advertised by financially interested parties) invariably generate also numerous subtle bad effects (the knowledge of which is routinely—though perhaps subconsciously —suppressed). It was the merit of *Silent Spring* that it forced biologists to institute a policy of total ecological accounting.

These, then, are the two principal influences that have affected the revision of this text. The first influence is most evident in Part I, where I have tried to present a fair and understandable picture of the molecular approach to problems of metabolism and heredity. In writing this section I have had my eye less on the embryonic specialist in molecular biology than I have on the future well-educated citizen whose need to know the difference between U-235 and U-238 is almost equalled by the necessity that he understand the functioning of messenger RNA. The concepts of molecular biology, at first sight difficult, actually simplify some of the great problems of biology. The scientific progress predictable from the application of these concepts during the next few years makes it imperative that all students learn this new vocabulary. ◄

Your reaction may be "Now that I read part of the Preface, what did I learn?" See if you can't answer that question by answering these questions:
 1. What two publications in the second half of the twentieth century turned biology in new directions?

 2. What effects have these two publications had on the revision of the text in question?

 3. True or False: The author says he is more concerned with writing for the future well-educated citizen than for the biological specialist.
 4. True or False: The author feels that knowledge of scientific terms such as U-235, U-238, and RNA is not imperative for the student.
The ability to answer these four questions reflects several important points for you. Questions 1 and 2 deal with the fact that the author is utilizing two important works in science as a guide for writing his book: Watson and Crick's "Molecular structure of nucleic acids" and Rachel Carson's *Silent Spring*. The first work represents the influence of molecular biology and the second work—more general, widely read, and controversial—redirected the attention of biologists to their civic responsibilities. The author states that such works as these have influenced biology in general and his text in particular.

Question 3 is true. The author says he is writing a book not for biology majors, but for the average educated citizen. Perhaps this is why the text is listed on the sample handout sheet for Biology 1, a course for non-science majors. Question 4 is false. The author does feel the future citizen will need to know the difference between such terms as U-235 and U-238. Thus, the Preface gives you some indication of the author's familiarity with the publications which influence his subject, plus the audience for whom his textbook is intended.

Now look at the Table of Contents of this biology text:

Contents[2]

---

[2]*Ibid.*

Notice that the book is divided into five parts. Compare these five divisions with the five units of the sample handout sheet for Biology 1. You can probably see what you will be covering each unit in class. These will be easy to relate to your textbook because of the similarity. But even more important is the mention of a bibliography, a glossary, answers to problems, and the 14 appendixes. As the course progresses, knowing that these aids are there may prove invaluable.

Some students think a book must be read from beginning to end. But a textbook, particularly in science, is more of a source book. It contains references to other works in case you wish to read more on a subject or in case you need references for reports (the bibliography). It contains an alphabetical list of words needed to understand the technical vocabulary used in the text (the glossary). It generally gives you charts, scales, measurements, and other basic factual information pertaining to the subject of the book (the appendixes). A good student constantly refers back to these aids to help him better understand his lectures and reading assignments. But he has to know they are there before he can use them.

Reading a science textbook can be difficult because it consists of descriptions of structures, formulas, and scientific measurements—a language all its own. But if you have explored your textbook thoroughly, you can lessen some of the difficulty by knowing where to look in the glossary, index, or appendix to find the answers you need.

Exploring a textbook also includes reading the introduction. Here is the Introduction to *Life: An Introduction to Biology* by Simpson and Beck.

► Introduction[3]

The picture introducing this part, which is itself an introduction to the whole book, is a photograph of a spider's web. The web is not alive, but it serves as a beautiful symbol of many of the general themes in the study of living things. It reflects the complexity and organization of the animal that made it. It has a function, which is to help provide food, and therefore both materials and energy, for the maintenance of the spider. It is the product of its maker's behavior. It expresses the intricacy and precision of the spider's adaptation—its ability to live from and within its environment; an aspect of that adaptation—and of all adaptations whatever—is the ability to reproduce, and hence to maintain a population of spiders through the ages, a population that endures although the individuals in it perish. The web is finally but preeminently an outcome of a history of change, of organic evolution, that started long, long before there were any spiders and that continues to produce extraordinary results.

These are the major themes of life and of this text, and we shall examine them further in Chapter 1 as they are seen in a forest and on

---

[3]From *Life: An Introduction to Biology*, 2nd ed., by George Gaylord Simpson and William S. Beck, © 1957, 1965, by Harcourt, Brace & World, Inc., and reproduced by their permission.

a coral reef. We shall then organize the inquiry to be pursued through-out the book in terms both of these main themes and of levels of organization in nature, from molecules through cells, whole organisms, specific populations, and multispecific communities to the entire world of living things in time and space.

Then we shall consider the nature of our inquiry and of science itself as a way of knowing, understanding, and coping with the world in which we live. We shall also briefly trace the expanding scope and impact of science to its culmination when Darwin at last brought the phenomena of life fully into the domain of naturalistic study. ◄

Notice how the authors tell you what the major themes of the book will be by using the analogy of a spider's web. The web, while not alive itself, is a symbol of many themes in the study of life: complexity and organization, function, maintenance, behavior, adaptability, reproduction, and evolution. These are the areas of life the book will explore.

The Introduction also tells you what is coming up in Chapter 1: an examination of life in a forest and life on a coral reef. The organization of the presentation will be from molecules in cells to organisms, to populations, to communities, to the world. Use this information to help you get your mind on Chapter 1. Use it to help you see where the chapter will take you. Use it to create an interest in the subject matter. Use it to be an active reader. And when you start reading that chapter, use the glossary, the appendix, and any other aids the book has to help you keep alert to the subject at hand.

Exploring lab manuals and workbooks

There is not much difference in technique between exploring lab manuals or workbooks and exploring textbooks. Usually, the lab manual is designed to provide work problems for use in lab situations. Rather than long stretches of reading, you get short directional or problem statements which you must work with and which you answer in the manual itself.

There are generally two types of reading material for lab work. One is the printed text itself, often a companion to the actual textbook. These manuals generally have prefaces or introductions, tables of contents, appendixes, and sometimes glossaries. If you are required to use such a manual, explore it just as you were shown in the previous pages. Compare the table of contents of the manual to that of the textbook. If possible, look over the work pages to see what type of equipment is called for.

The other type of reading material for lab work is the teacher-made handout sheet. Many instructors prefer to make up their own lab exercises to coincide with the textbook being used. Here is an example of a teacher-made lab exercise:

LAB EXERCISE #1

Cell Life

Assignment: Read Chapter 2.

Purpose of exercise: **(1)**   to examine the way plant and animal cells
duplicate
(2)   to study the various forms

Equipment: Microslide-viewer and microslides. Pick up the viewer
assigned to your lab desk and one each of the following:

(1)   Set 53 - Animal mitosis
(2)   Set 55 - Plant mitosis
(3)   Set 10 - Cells of the body
(4)   Set 11 - Cells of plants

Exercises: Chapter 1 discussed how nearly all cells duplicate by a
process called <u>mitosis</u>. The states of mitosis you will
view on the slides are part of a continuous process.

A.   <u>Mitosis in the onion root tip (Allium)</u>. Remove the
microslide from its slot in Set 55 - Plant Mitosis and
insert it in the slot on the right side of the viewer.
Follow the directions in the microslide folder.

1.   <u>Early Prophase</u>. Read the description in the folder
for this stage. Make a sketch of this stage (Cell **A**)
in the space below:

Normally, handout sheets such as these run from four to six pages. If
these sheets are given to you *before* the day of your lab session, explore
them by making certain you have read the correct assignment, that you
understand the purpose of the exercises, and that you have looked over all
the activities you will be expected to do. When you arrive in lab, you will
be ready to go to work or you will already know the questions you need to
ask your instructor before you can get to work.

If these sheets are given to you *on* the day of the lab session, then be
certain to look over all pages before beginning your first exercise. This
will prevent mistakes caused by not fully understanding the experiment
before you started it.

If this chapter seems to be devoted to biology rather than to all sciences, this is done only for illustrative purposes. All science textbooks and lab manuals should be explored as explained here. Open your science textbook and lab manual right now. Explore both by following the textbook-exploring steps presented in the summary that follows. Chapter 2 will show you how to explore specific reading assignments.

SUMMARY

The purpose of this chapter is to show you how and why you should explore your textbooks and lab manuals. Exploring is a preparation or familiarization step to help you get organized for careful reading. Explore your textbooks by:

(1) reading the title page and copyright page
(2) reading the preface
(3) reading the introduction
(4) reading the table of contents
(5) familiarizing yourself with glossaries, appendixes, and indexes

Once you have done this, you will understand how the textbook is structured, what the author's purpose is for this structure, and how you can best use the book to help you better understand the information it contains.

You may now want to turn to the exercises on pages 167 – 171 to practice more exploring.

2

Exploring Your Assignments

The total picture. Chapter 1 discussed why and how to explore your textbooks. This chapter deals with exploring specific reading assignments in the textbooks, in lab manuals, and in outside sources. *Before* reading this chapter carefully, read the bold headings and the summary. This will help get your mind on the subject of the chapter. Remember that this chapter deals with only one aspect of the four-step reading process.

Exploring textbook assignments

Because many students feel the pressures of heavy reading assignments, they often sign up for speed-reading courses which they hope will help them read hundreds or thousands of words per minute. Except in rare cases, such a goal is not achieved. Readers can only read as fast as they can assimilate and think about what they are reading. While some materials — newspapers, magazines, novels — can be read rapidly, materials such as science textbooks must be read thoughtfully, critically, and slowly.

But slowly doesn't mean a plodding word-by-word pace. At some points in your reading you are able to read very rapidly. The snail's pace may begin when your mind starts wandering off the subject, and precious time is lost. That's where exploring an assignment or article begins to help.

Before you can read something thoughtfully and critically, you must clear your mind and prepare it to accept the reading matter. If you don't, the chances are good that you will become bored or frustrated as you try to plow through your reading assignments.

To help combat this problem, many textbooks are set up like this one. A section similar to *The total picture* gives you an overview of the chapter, connects it with the previous chapter, and prepares you to read. The subheadings give you the major sections of the chapter, and the summary lists the major points that have been made.

Do you use these aids to your advantage? Exploring a chapter like this is a snap. Before reading carefully, you should read *The total picture*, the subheadings, and the summary. That's right. Read the summary *before* reading the entire chapter. This alerts you to the major points of the chapter. Of course, after you've read the chapter carefully, the summary should be read again to help you remember or pull together the major points.

Sometimes a textbook will not have overviews, subheadings, or summaries as such; but it may have questions at the end. Another practical exploring method is to read those questions before reading the chapter. A good look at them can give you a purpose for reading. Having specific questions in mind as you read will help control your concentration. If you don't know some of the key words used in the questions, you can look them up in the glossary before reading carefully, thus making your reading a bit easier and faster. It also helps to look at the pictures and diagrams and to read the captions under them as you explore. Whatever you know about the subject will be recalled; or if the information is totally new, questions will almost automatically pop into your head: "What is *that*?" or "Why does that occur under those circumstances?" Questions like these can be used as purposes for reading.

Here is a chapter reprinted from a science text. Try exploring this chapter by the methods just described. Don't read it—just explore.

▶   ## A Few Basic Physical and Chemical Principles[1]

Explanations of the activities of living organisms have been found by the application of various concepts common to the fields of physics and chemistry. Obviously, a knowledge of these concepts is essential to an understanding of such explanations.

Molecular structure

All matter (that which has mass and occupies space) is composed of submicroscopic particles, called **molecules**, which are in continuous motion. Such molecules are the smallest subdivision of a substance* which still possesses all of the specific properties or characteristics of that substance. Since these particles are not visible, their motility has been determined by various indirect methods.

---

[1]Reprinted with permission of The Macmillan Company from *Botany: A Functional Approach* by Walter H. Muller. © by W. Muller 1963.

*Substance: a material all samples of which have the same set of properties; it consists of but one kind of molecule.

However, a visible indication that water molecules are moving can be obtained by observing what has been termed **Brownian movement**. If small but visible particles (such as India ink) are suspended in a drop of water and observed through a microscope, these particles will be seen to "jiggle" about. Their non-directional trembling movement is not a result of their own molecular composition but of the motion of water molecules striking first from one direction and then from another. The unequal collisions push the ink particles first to one side and then to another.

The molecules of any material are attracted to each other in varying degrees, and this greatly influences the amount of motility of individual molecules. In solids molecules are strongly attracted, resulting in little movement. In liquids the attraction is less, molecular motion is greater, and the material is fluid. The molecules of a gas have very little attraction for each other, the individual molecules have great motility, and these molecules will move farther and farther apart until the gas completely fills the space available to it. This movement of molecules from one area to another is termed **diffusion** and is a result of the inherent continuous movement of all molecules.

Molecules in turn are composed of **atoms**, the building blocks, which are the smallest particles that will enter into a chemical reaction. Recent evidence indicates that atomic structure is more complicated than had been suspected, but for our purpose we may consider an atom to be made up of a sphere or swarm of **electrons** (negatively charged particles) surrounding a positively charged core.† The positive charge is due to **protons** (discrete units of positive charge), but the core also contains particles having no charge at all, the **neutrons**. This central portion contains practically the entire mass of the atom but occupies an extremely tiny portion of the volume; practically all the volume is occupied by electrons. In a neutral atom, the negative charge of the electrons is exactly balanced by the positive charge of the core; the number of electrons is equal to the number of protons. When an electron is removed from a neutral atom, the particle which remains behind is positively charged, or a **positive ion**:

$$Na \rightarrow Na^+ + e^-$$

The electron is shown as e^-. When a neutral atom picks up an electron, it forms a **negative ion**:

$$Cl + e^- \rightarrow Cl^-$$

---

†The term "nucleus" (rather than "core") is used by physicists and chemists, but this might lead to confusion in the mind of a beginning biology student who is more familiar with a cellular nucleus than with an atomic nucleus.

The symbols Na and Cl refer to sodium and chlorine respectively. Such symbols are the chemists' method of abbreviating the name of an **element**, a substance which cannot be decomposed into simpler substances by ordinary action. Table 2.1 indicates some of the elements which are important in cellular structure and function.

Table 2.1. Elements Important to Cell Structure and Function

Element	Symbol	Element	Symbol
Boron	B	Magnesium	Mg
Calcium	Ca	Manganese	Mn
Carbon	C	Molybdenum	Mo
Chlorine°	Cl	Nitrogen	N
Cobalt°	Co	Oxygen	O
Copper	Cu	Phosphorus	P
Fluorine°	F	Potassium	K
Hydrogen	H	Sodium°	Na
Iodine°	I	Sulfur	S
Iron	Fe	Zinc	Zn

°These elements are essential for animals, but they have not been proved to be essential for plants. Quite possibly more elements will be added to this list as investigations produce further data (see Section 15.1).

Compounds and formulae

Some substances are **compounds**: they are capable of being decomposed into simpler substances. Water can be broken down into its constituents, hydrogen and oxygen, but the latter two materials are elements, which cannot be decomposed further. In order to indicate the composition of a compound, a **formula** is written (e.g., H_2O). The formula, utilizing symbols and subscripts, provides the following information: (1) the elements in the compound; (2) the relative number of each atom (subscripts indicate the number of atoms, the number 1 being omitted); (3) the combining weights of the elements, since the symbol refers to an atom and the atomic weights are known; and (4) the molecular weight of the compound, if it is known.

Many compounds are found within plants, but only three of these will be mentioned now. **Carbohydrates** (e.g., sugars, starch, cellulose) are composed of carbon (C), hydrogen (H), and oxygen (O), with the last two occurring in a two-to-one ratio as in water (H_2O). Molecules of the simple sugar glucose ($C_6H_{12}O_6$) are frequently combined by the cell to form more complex carbohydrates, such as starch, which are then stored in the cell. Later these complex molecules may be broken down to simple sugars and utilized. **Fats and oils** are also composed only of carbon, hydrogen, and oxygen, but relatively little oxygen is found in proportion to the other two atoms—as, for example, in stearin $C_{57}H_{120}O_6$. At ordinary room temperature, oils are liquids while fats are solids, but there is no general chemical distinction between them. The breakdown of fats and oils results in the production of fatty acids and glycerol (see Section 11.4). **Proteins** contain carbon, hydrogen, oxygen, nitrogen (N), frequently sulfur (S), and sometimes phosphorus (P), as in milk casein $C_{708}H_{1130}N_{180}O_{224}S_4P_4$. These are the most complex molecules found in living cells and can be broken down to simpler substances known as amino acids. Just as complex compounds can be broken down to simpler ones, they can also be synthesized from the simple compounds by living cells. Such complex compounds are usually important constituents of the protoplasm, or they may be storage products.

Ionization

When dissolved in water, the molecules of many materials will separate into two electrically charged particles, called ions. Common table salt is composed of sodium (Na) and chlorine (Cl) and ionizes, or dissociates, as follows:

$$NaCl \rightarrow Na^+ + Cl^-$$

The plus and minus charges balance. The charged particles are atoms, as above, or groups of atoms, as in the carbonate ion $(CO_3^=)$ below:

$$Na_2CO_3 \text{ (sodium carbonate)} \rightarrow 2Na^+ + CO_3^=$$

Such ions are separately mobile and are highly reactive. All acids ionize to form hydrogen ions (H^+):

$$HCl \text{ (hydrochloric acid)} \rightarrow H^+ + Cl^-$$
$$H_2SO_4 \text{ (sulfuric acid)} \rightarrow 2H^+ + SO_4^=$$

All bases dissociate to form hydroxyl ions (OH^-):

$$NaOH \text{ (sodium hydroxide)} \rightarrow Na^+ + OH^-$$
$$Ba(OH)_2 \text{ (barium hydroxide)} \rightarrow Ba^{++} + 2OH^-$$

When acids and bases are mixed, they are neutralized, in that the H^+ ions and the OH^- ions combine to form water (H_2O), which is only very slightly dissociated. During neutralization, salts are formed:

$$HCl + NaOH \rightarrow H_2O + NaCl \text{ (a salt)}$$

Salts do not form either H^+ or OH^- ions when they ionize.

Oxidation and reduction

When coal is burned, oxygen combines with the carbon, carbon dioxide (CO_2) is formed, and the chemically bound energy[11] in the coal is liberated as heat and light. The combination of oxygen with other elements and the consequent release of energy was the original meaning of the term oxidation. However, many oxidations occur, especially in living cells, where free oxygen is not involved—sometimes there is a loss of hydrogens, sometimes a loss of electrons. The basic characteristic of an **oxidation** is that there is a loss of electrons. As far as the living cell is concerned, the important result of oxidation is that bound energy (as in a food molecule) is liberated or made available.

Whenever one material is oxidized, another is reduced. **Reduction** refers to the gain of electrons (sometimes in the form of the addition of hydrogen). In other words, the electrons which are lost when a substance is oxidized are accepted by the substance which is reduced.

Hydrolysis and condensation

The breakdown and the production of complex compounds that occur so frequently in living cells are actually examples of hydrolyses and condensations. The **digestion** of a complex starch molecule to sugar molecules actually utilizes water and thus is a type of **hydrolysis**—one molecule of water is added for every molecule of sugar that is produced:

$$\text{Starch} + n\ H_2O \rightarrow n\ \text{Sugar}$$

The symbol "n" is used because the size of the starch molecule is unknown, and so the number of water molecules used and the number of sugar molecules produced are unknown. The reverse process, whereby a large number of sugar molecules combine to form starch, with the attendant elimination of water molecules, is termed **condensation** or **synthesis.** Fats, oils, and proteins undergo similar syntheses and hydrolyses.

---

[11]Energy is anything that can be converted into work (e.g., heat, electricity, or the potential energy of a coiled spring) or the ability to do work.

Adsorption, capillarity, and imbibition

The molecules of many substances are **polar**, that is, the atoms which make up the molecules join in an angular fashion so that, though the over-all negative and positive charges balance, certain portions of the molecule are more negative and other portions are more positive. This is true of water molecules (H_2O), which should be represented as

H⠀⠀⠀⠀H
⠀\⠀⠀⠀/
⠀⠀⠀O⠀⠀⠀⠀⠀⠀⠀and not as H—O—H.

Many materials have charged areas, and molecules or ions are frequently concentrated, or held, on various surfaces, a phenomenon termed **adsorption**. For example, the clay particles of soil are negatively charged and hence attract and hold water and positively charged ions. This characteristic of soil particles is of tremendous importance to the growth of plants and will be emphasized in Section 16.4.

If the tip of a tube of small diameter is immersed in water, as in Figure 2.1, the level of water in the tube will rise higher than the

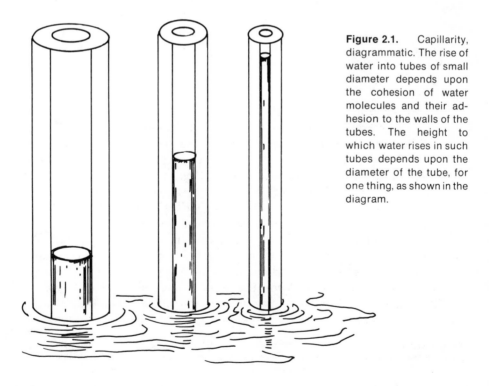

Figure 2.1. Capillarity, diagrammatic. The rise of water into tubes of small diameter depends upon the cohesion of water molecules and their adhesion to the walls of the tubes. The height to which water rises in such tubes depends upon the diameter of the tube, for one thing, as shown in the diagram.

surface into which the tube was placed. Such a rise of water in tubes, termed **capillary action** or **capillarity**, depends upon the cohesion of water molecules to each other and the adhesion of water molecules to the tube walls.** The smaller the diameter of the tube, the higher will be the capillary rise.

The swelling of dry wood when it is placed in water results from the diffusion of water into the wood, the capillary action of water entering tiny cracks, crevices, and tubes of the wood, and the entrance of water between the particles of wood and its adhesion to these particles. **Imbibition** is this entrance of water into solids and the resultant swelling. The wood particles are forced farther and farther apart as the water enters, and the swelling forces may be considerable. The granite blocks used to build ancient pyramids were probably quarried by drilling holes in the stone, pounding dry wood tightly into these holes, and then pouring water on the wood. The resultant imbibitional forces split the granite. Leaky rowboats may become watertight when placed in water, due to the swelling of the dry wood. In a similar manner a door may stick as atmospheric humidity rises and the wooden door, or even the door jamb, swells. When a seed germinates, the imbibitional forces resulting from water absorption are sufficient to rupture the tough seed coat, allowing the enclosed embryo to grow. Proteins swell much more than starch which swells more than cellulose. Therefore, the storage tissues of seeds (which contain much protein and starch) swell more than the seed coats.

Surface-to-volume ratio

Adsorption and absorption are both dependent to a great extent upon exposed surfaces. In the former phenomenon, materials are held to surfaces, whereas in absorption materials pass through a surface. Therefore, the greater the amount of surface, the more adsorption and absorption will take place, other factors being equal. For example, a convoluted soil particle will adsorb more water molecules than a spherical soil particle of similar composition and volume because of the greater surface area in the former.

In general, the smaller or the more convoluted a structure, the greater is the surface-to-volume ratio. A simple way of visualizing this is to think of your textbook, which has a certain volume and six surfaces when closed. When the book is opened to expose each of the pages individually, the volume is unchanged, but the exposed surface area has increased tremendously, just as with any convoluted

---

**Cohesion refers to the attraction of similar molecules to each other (e.g., water molecule to water molecule). Adhesion refers to the attraction between dissimilar molecules (e.g., water molecule to molecule of tube wall).

structure. If the pages are torn out, the total volume does not change, but each page now has surfaces exposed. In effect, the extremely small soil particles, which have developed by disintegration of large particles, are similar to the torn book.

The importance of this principle of surface-to-volume (S/V) ratio will be emphasized several times throughout the text.

Summary

1. All matter is composed of molecules, which are in continuous motion. Spheres of electrons surrounding a central core constitute the atoms of which molecules are composed.

2. Molecules may separate into electrically charged ions.

3. Oxidations provide the energy which is required for normal functioning of the cell.

4. Hydrolysis is the splitting of complex molecules to simpler ones with the utilization of water. Digestions are hydrolyses. Condensations, or syntheses, are the reverse of hydrolyses.

5. Adsorption is the concentration of molecules or ions on surfaces due to the forces of attraction between them. Imbibition refers to the entrance of water into solids and the resultant swelling.

6. The surface-to-volume ratio of structures is important in the processes of adsorption and absorption.

Review Topics and Questions

1. How could you determine whether the movement of particles in a drop of water was Brownian motion or not?

2. Describe a procedure that you could use to demonstrate diffusion.

3. The starch content of a cell increases while the amount of starch in a neighboring cell decreases. Since there is no other source of carbohydrate, the first cell presumably is obtaining materials from the second cell. Starch is not soluble and cannot penetrate membranes or plasmodesmata. Explain how the observed phenomena are possible if the assumption is correct.

4. List six elements and explain how each is important to living cells.

5. Discuss the advantages of utilizing symbols and formulae, as the chemist does when discussing reactions that occur within a cell.

6. A cube with dimensions of one centimeter is divided into smaller cubes with one millimeter dimensions. What was the original volume? The final volume? What was the original surface area? The final surface area?

Suggested readings

Orear, J. *Fundamental Physics*. New York: Wiley, 1961.
Selwood, P. W. *General Chemistry*. New York: Holt-Dryden, 1959. ◄

Now see how well you explored this chapter by answering these questions:

1. T or F: There is a summary at the end of the chapter.
2. T or F: There are questions at the end of the chapter.
3. T or F: There are suggested readings at the end of the chapter.
4. T or F: The chapter has subdivisions.

It doesn't take much exploring to know all the above statements are true. But what's even more important is how well you used the aids mentioned in the questions. See how well you can answer the next questions without looking back:

1. Circle all the following topics you remember seeing mentioned as you explored.
   a. Molecular structure   e. Hydrolysis
   b. Macular ibodents   f. Adsorption
   c. Ionization   g. Chemistry of plant life
   d. Oxidation   h. Surface-to-volume ratio
2. How many points of importance are listed in the summary?
   a. four   c. six
   b. five   d. seven
3. T or F: The following is one of the questions listed at the end of the chapter: "How could you determine whether the movement of particles in a drop of water has Brownian motion or not?"
4. The title of the chapter is _____.

Compare your answers with these. In question 1, all but items *b* and *g* are subheadings in the chapter, and should have been circled. In question 2, *c* is the correct answer: the summary contains six major points. Question 3 is a true statement; the question is the first at the end of the chapter. The answer to question 4 is "A Few Basic Physical and Chemical Principles."

Knowing these things is not important in itself. It's how you use this knowledge gained from exploring that is important. If you were now to read this chapter carefully, you would be better able to control your concentration and comprehension by

(1) reading to find the answers to the questions so that you have a purpose for reading.

(2) reading to understand the subheadings well enough to define them.

(3) reading to make certain you understand the significance of the six summary points in relation to the title of the chapter. More will be said in

later chapters about how to read thoroughly and critically. Right now the important thing is learning how to explore before reading.

You probably have a reading assignment in one of your science text-books. Before attempting a thorough reading, try exploring it using the techniques you just applied here.

Exploring via the visual aids

Almost every science textbook contains a wealth of pictorial materials — graphs, charts, tables, diagrams, photographs, and the like. These visual aids are there to make your reading task easier.

When you explore a reading assignment, look over all of the tables and illustrations. They present information in the form of a pattern or a picture, and such a presentation is usually easier to grasp than words alone. This is another good way to get a feeling for what the assignment is all about.

Exploring your lab-manual assignments

Because lab manuals and workbooks are usually filled with directions for experiments, it is necessary to explore them differently. It is always a good idea to read over the experiments you will have to do in lab before you get there. This isn't always possible, however, so before attempting to do the experiment, look over the directions, read the captions on any diagrams, and look to see if there is going to be any writing involved. Exploring lab-manual assignments should be done a little more thoroughly than reading chapter assignments because it requires step-by-step procedures.

Here is a short selection from a biology lab manual. Don't try to read it carefully, but explore it *quickly* to determine what equipment you'll need and what you are expected to do.

▶ ## Blood[2]

Put a drop of undiluted frog's blood on a slide and cover. Note the size and shape of the red blood cells and the presence of a nucleus. In order to see the white cells more easily, add a drop of acetic acid at the edge of the cover slip. (This treatment destroys the red blood cells, thus making the white cells easier to find.) Why are some white blood cells called *phagocytes*? What is their function?

If you want to study your own blood cells, rinse the pad of your middle finger with alcohol; stab with a sharp scalpel blade mounted

---

[2]From *Experiments in General Biology* by Graham DuShane and David Regnery (San Francisco: W. H. Freeman and Company, 1958), pp. 40-41.

in a cork as shown in Figure 2.2. Wipe off the first drop of blood and squeeze out another. Touch the second drop lightly to the surface of a slide. Cover and examine as for the frog's blood. Do your blood cells differ from those of a frog in shape, size, and presence or absence of a nucleus? Add acetic acid as before and find the white cells. ◀

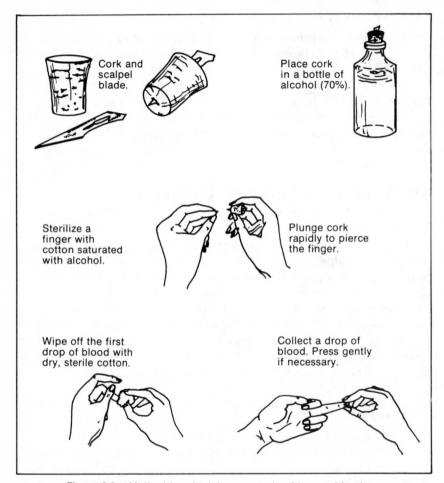

Cork and scalpel blade.

Place cork in a bottle of alcohol (70%).

Sterilize a finger with cotton saturated with alcohol.

Plunge cork rapidly to pierce the finger.

Wipe off the first drop of blood with dry, sterile cotton.

Collect a drop of blood. Press gently if necessary.

Figure 2.2.   Method for obtaining a sample of human blood.

Check how well you explored by answering these questions:
1. Which of the following will you need for conducting the experiment?
   a. undiluted frog's blood
   b. acetic acid
   c. syringe
   d. cork
   e. scalpel
   f. alcohol
   g. gauge
   h. microscope
2. The purpose of the experiment is

a. to study red and white blood cells.

b. to compare your blood cells with a frog's.

c. both *a* and *b*.

3. T or F: You will be required to answer questions about your experiment.

In question 1, all but *c* and *g* will be required for the experiment. (You can assume that a microscope will be needed to examine the slides of blood.) The answer to question two is *c*. The third question is true. Here again, knowing these answers is only as important as your ability to use them. Once you have explored this lab assignment and gathered your materials, you are ready to read carefully, step by step, the procedure for conducting the experiment. Remember, exploring is preparation for careful reading.

The lab work usually clarifies the concepts presented in the textbook by demonstrating them. If the lab work gets ahead of the textbook reading and class lectures, as sometimes happens, it may be harder to see the point of what you are doing in the lab. You may have to explore the next section in the textbook or ask your instructor to explain the concepts being dealt with in the lab.

Exploring reading assignments from outside sources

Remember the Biology 1 handout sheet used in Chapter 1? If you do, you may recall that the instructor required outside reading reports. A list of journals was provided for you. Most science instructors require that you read from journals because they supply additional material not available in the textbook. Such an assignment to some students means hours at the library trying to find articles that they can understand well enough to write a report.

Here is a time-saving exploring method that will help you do two things: determine whether or not you want to read the article and prepare your mind for reading it if you decide to. The best way to explore outside reading assignments is to follow these steps:

(1) read the title of the article, and ask yourself its significance.

(2) read the first paragraph or two, depending on the length of the paragraphs, carefully. Usually the point of the article is stated in the opening paragraph.

(3) read only the first sentence of each of the succeeding paragraphs until you get to the last paragraph. Usually the main idea of each paragraph can be detected.

(4) read the last paragraph carefully. Perhaps the reason for exploring an article this way can best be shown with an example. Try these four steps on the following article from *Science*. Remember, don't read it all; merely explore it.

► Size-Detecting Mechanisms in Human Vision[3]

Allan Pantle and Robert Sekuler

Abstract. *Inspecting a pattern of alternating dark and light bars makes it difficult to see a similar pattern presented afterward. This phenomenon can be used to isolate mechanisms responsive to bars of a given width. Our results suggest that the human visual system contains several different classes of size detectors, each maximally sensitive to visual targets with sizes in a particular range.*

The ability to appreciate the size of an object is a basic visual perceptual function, and much research has been concerned with the indirect or higher-order processes contributing to this ability (1). We tried to determine whether, in addition to use of these indirect cues, the human visual system can directly encode the area of retinal images produced by objects of different sizes.

The observation of a pattern of alternating dark and light bars reduces the visibility of a similar pattern presented thereafter (2). This phenomenon may be exploited to isolate mechanisms responding to patterns whose bars are of a particular size. One measure of the size of a bar in a pattern of alternating light and dark bars is the number of such alternating pairs (or cycles) occupying a given area. This quantity is termed spatial frequency, with values expressed in number of cycles per degree (cycle/deg) of visual angle. In our experiment the threshold for gratings with different spatial frequencies was measured after adaptation to gratings of various spatial frequencies. It is assumed that the ability of an adaptation pattern with a given spatial frequency to affect the visibility of a test grating with the same or some other spatial frequency reflects the extent to which the perception of both gratings depends on common mechanisms. A description of the spatial-frequency responsivity (or tuning) of the mechanism mediating the perception of a test grating of a given spatial frequency can be obtained by an analysis of the interactions between that test grating and adaptation gratings with various spatial frequencies.

Eleven different adaptation patterns were used in our experiment. Ten were photographic square-wave gratings with horizontal bars whose spatial frequencies, at the observer's eye, were 0.18, 0.35, 0.70, 1.05, 1.40, 2.10, 2.80, 3.50, 10.12, and 22.00 cycle/deg. The luminance of a light bar of any grating was 1.35 ft lam (1 ft lam = .92 m lam); that of each dark bar was 0.45 ft lam. The 11th adaptation pat-

[3]From *Science*, Vol. 162 (December 6, 1968), 1146-1148. Copyright 1968 by the American Association for the Advancement of Science.

tern was a uniform field whose luminance was equivalent to that of the mean luminance of the grating patterns, 0.90 ft lam. All fields were presented in Maxwellian view to the observer's right eye by a four-channel optical system (3). Each circular adaptation field subtended a visual angle of 9° and had a small, dark, central fixation point.

For the first 4 minutes of every experimental session the observer inspected one of the 11 adaptation patterns. The same pattern remained visible to the observer for the entire session except for brief periods when test grating targets were presented. To minimize the development of negative after-images of the grating bars, the adapting pattern was mechanically shifted every 3 seconds by one-half cycle, interchanging the dark and light bars. Within each session two independent determinations were made of the luminance threshold for each of three different test gratings, 0.35, 1.05, and 3.50 cycle/deg. These test gratings were oriented horizontally and appeared in the same part of the visual field as the adaptation patterns.

The following was the sequence of events on each trial. The adaptation pattern was extinguished for 0.7 second (interval 1); it reappeared for the following 1.5 seconds and was extinguished again for another period (interval 2) of 0.7 second. The adaptation pattern was presented again, remaining on for the next 9.1 seconds. The entire sequence was begun again for the next trial. The test grating was presented, superposed on a homogeneous background of 0.58 ft lam, either in interval 1 or in interval 2. It occurred with equal frequency in the two intervals according to a random schedule. The interval without the test grating contained only the homogeneous background. The observer had to identify the interval containing the test grating. If this identification was wrong, the luminance of the light bars of the test grating was increased by 0.1 log unit for the presentation on the next trial. If identification was correct on three successive trials, the luminance was reduced by 0.1 log unit for the next trial. These rules for adjusting luminance to match the observer's performance generate a series of data points which bracket the stimulus value corresponding to the 79.4-percent point on the traditional "frequency of seeing" curve (4). Each series was begun with a randomly chosen luminance for the test bars, and continued until the occurrence of five reversals in the direction of change in luminance (either decreasing to increasing, or vice versa). The threshold in a series was defined as the mean luminance of the light bars of the test grating for the last four of the five reversals in that series. Each of the two observers was tested in 22 sessions, giving four independent determinations of threshold for each of the 33 combinations of adaptation and test patterns.

Figures 2.3 and 2.4 show the mean threshold luminance of the

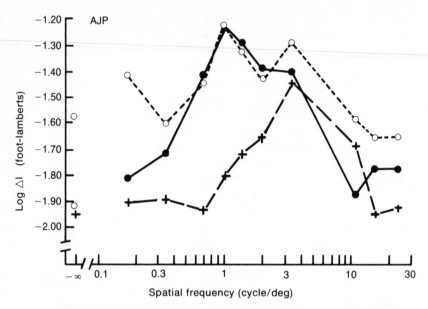

Figure 2.3. Luminance threshold for test gratings of various spatial frequencies as a function of the spatial frequency of the adaptation grating. Data obtained with a test grating of 0.35 cycle/deg are indicated by unfilled circles; 1/05 cycle/deg, filled circles; and 3.50 cycle/deg, crosses. Data from observer A.P.

light bars of the test target as a function of the spatial frequency of the adaptation grating. Any individual function describes the change in the threshold for a test grating of a particular spatial frequency as the spatial frequency of the adaptation grating was varied. To make statistical comparisons between the shapes of the functions, we made three separate analyses of variance. In each analysis the data obtained with a different pair of test targets were compared, and data for both observers were entered in each analysis. The analysis of variance term of interest represents the interaction between the spatial frequencies of the adaptation and test patterns. This term reflects the statistical significance of the difference between the shapes of any two test target functions.

The shape of the threshold function for the test grating of 3.5 cycle/deg differed from that obtained with test grating of 0.35 cycle/deg ($F = 3.19$, d.f. $= 10,10$; $P < .05$); it also differed from that obtained with the test grating of 1.05 cycle/deg ($F = 8.26$, d.f. $= 10,10$; $P < .01$). One obvious difference among these threshold functions is the location of their peaks. Whereas the peaks of the threshold functions for the test gratings of 0.35 and 1.05 cycle/deg occurred with the adaptation grating of 1.05 cycle/deg, the peak of the threshold function for the test grating of 3.5 cycle/deg occurred at a higher spatial frequency of the adaptation grating. This implies that the spatial-frequency tuning of the respective mechanisms is different.

In contrast to the above, the functions for the test gratings of 0.35 and 1.05 cycle/deg have nearly identical shapes ($F = 1.31$, d.f. = 10,10; $P > .25$), suggesting that the spatial-frequency tuning of the mechanisms mediating the detection of the gratings is similar. This latter finding suggests that the number of differentially tuned classes of spatial-frequency mechanisms is limited.

These conclusions are similar to those reached by Campbell and Robson (5) from a Fourier analysis of the visibility of gratings of different spatial frequencies and waveforms. The spatial filters, identified by our method and by that of Campbell and Robson, could derive from cells in the visual system as described by Enroth-Cugell and Robson (6); each of these cells, because of the organization and size of its receptive field, tends to be maximally responsive to a grating of a particular spatial frequency.

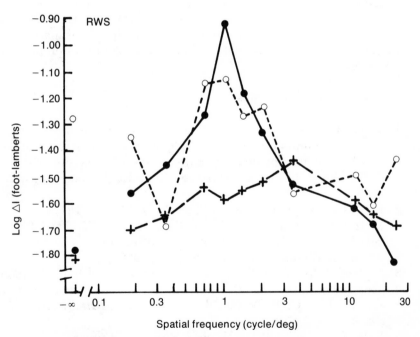

Figure 2.4. Luminance thresholds for test gratings of various spatial frequencies as a function of the spatial frequency of the adaptation grating. Data obtained with a test grating of 0.35 cycle/deg are indicated by unfilled circles; 1.05 cycle/deg, filled circles; and 3.50 cycle/deg, crosses. Data from observer R. S.

In addition to their possible involvement in the perception of spatial extent, spatial filters may function differentially in the perception of targets moving at different speeds. Pantle (3) measured the luminance threshold for a moving test grating of constant spatial frequency presented after the observer had viewed a stationary-adaptation grating having one of a number of different spatial frequencies. Although adaptation gratings with low-spatial frequencies raised the threshold for fast-moving test gratings, adaptation gratings with high-spatial frequencies were needed to raise the threshold for slowly moving test gratings. This relation between the spatial frequency of the adaptation grating and the speed of the test grating suggests that spatial filters sensitive to large areas (low-spatial frequencies) are particularly involved in the perception of quickly moving targets; filters sensitive to small areas (high-spatial frequencies) are particularly involved in the perception of slowly moving targets.

Spatial filters of the kind measured in our experiment may also contribute to the phenomenon of size constancy. When an object moves toward or away from an observer, the size of the retinal image of that object varies. The fact that phenomenal size, under a variety of conditions, remains relatively unchanged is the central fact of size constancy. Richards' (7) model of size constancy postulates shifts, during accommodation and convergence, among sets of spatial filters which, like those we have described, are tuned to different retinal image areas.

References and Notes

1. These higher-order processes include assumptions about size, in the case of familiar objects, and judgments based on the context in which an object appears. For a discussion of these processes, see J. Hochberg, *Perception* (Prentice-Hall, Englewood Cliffs, N.J., 1964).
2. F. W. Campbell and J. K. Kulikowsky, *J. Physiol.* **187**, 437 (1966); K. Houlihan and R. Sekuler, *J. Exp. Psychol.* **77**, 281 (1968); R. Sekuler, *J. Exp. Psychol.* **70**, 401 (1965); R. Sekuler, E. Rubin, W. Cushman, *J. Opt. Soc. Amer.* **58**, 1146 (1968).
3. A. Pantle, thesis, Northwestern University, Evanston, Ill. (1968).
4. This technique is fully described, and its advantages are amplified by G. B. Wetherill and H. Levitt, *Brit. J. Math. Stat. Psychol.* **18**, 1 (1965).
5. F. W. Campbell and J. Robson, *J. Physiol.*, in press.
6. C. Enroth-Cugell and J. Robson, *ibid.* **187**, 517 (1966).
7. W. Richards, *Neuropsychologia* **5**, 63 (1967).
8. Supported by National Institute of Neurological Diseases and Blindness grant NB-06354 to R. S. ◄

If you followed the four exploring steps, you should be able to answer these questions:

(1) The object of the study was to find out
   a. why looking at a pattern of alternating dark and light bars makes it harder to see a similar pattern presented afterward.
   b. whether the human visual system can directly encode the area of retinal images produced by objects of different sizes.
   c. how many different classes of size detectors are contained in the human visual system.

(2) T or F: When an object moves toward or away from an observer, the size of the retinal image remains constant.

(3) T or F: Shifts among sets of spatial filters may explain the phenomenon of size constancy.

Compare your answers with these: (1) b; (2) F; (3) T.

The answer to question 1 is contained in the first paragraph of the article (after the abstract). The words "We tried to determine whether . . ." should have served as a signal to you. Always look for the key concept or the chief purpose of a study.

The answers to questions 2 and 3 can be found in the final paragraph. If you followed the exploring steps, you should not have had any difficulty with these questions.

Now that you have explored (but not read) this article, you know at least two things: what it is about and whether or not you want to read it. If you decide you do want to read it, you are prepared to read because you know how long the article is and how long it will take you to read it, what the basic point is, and some questions for which you will seek answers as you read.

Try this exploring approach the next time you read an article from a magazine or journal. But remember, going through the motions of exploring isn't what's important, it's *using* what you can learn by exploring for your reading purpose.

SUMMARY

This chapter shows you how to explore, as a preparation for close reading, three different types of reading assignment: textbooks, lab manuals, and outside sources.

Chapter assignments should be explored by reading the title, the opening comments, all boldface (main) headings, the summary, and any questions at the end of the chapter.

Lab-manual reading assignments require more thorough exploring by looking quickly over the entire assignment to see what materials you will need and what you are expected to accomplish. This enables you to gather equipment and organize yourself so that you can carefully follow the step-by-step directions in the lab manual.

Reading assignments in outside sources are usually articles from journals. Four exploring steps are recommended: (1) read the title of the article and ask yourself its significance; (2) read the first paragraph carefully; (3) read only the first sentence of each paragraph until you get to the last one; and (4) read the last paragraph carefully.

These exploring procedures all help create purposes for reading beyond the fact that they are assignments you have to do if you want to pass the course. But the procedure is only as good as your willingness to make it work.

You may now want to turn to the exercises on pages 173–185 to practice the three types of exploring discussed in this chapter.

TWO

Check the Vocabulary

Even poetry can be hard to read. Try this:

> cwædon þæt he wære   woruld-cyning
> mannum mildust   and mon-þwærust,
> leódum liðost   and lof-geornost.

or how about this:

> Whan that Aprille with his shoures sóote
> The droghte of Marche hath percéd to the roote,
> And bathed every veyne in swich licour,
> Of which vertu engendred is the flour;

Maybe you prefer the following:

> k ≡ R/N

Contrary to what you may be thinking, each of the above examples is English in one form or another. The first example is taken from *Beowulf*, the first great English poem. It was written in Old English sometime before the year 750. The second example is from Chaucer's *Canterbury Tales*, written about 1386 in what is known as Middle English. And the last example is a chemical formula taken from a contemporary chemistry textbook.

In each case, your ability to understand the examples has nothing to do with your intelligence. You simply lack the vocabulary necessary to understand what is being said. If you knew what *mildust*, *shoures*, or R/N meant, you could easily read the examples, just as you are easily reading this Preface because you know most of the words being used. But for many students science becomes almost a foreign language because they lack the understanding of words like *exophthalmic*, *atony*, *ophthalmoscope*, and *blastomere*.

Check the Vocabulary is the second of four steps in a process for better

reading. In some ways it may be the most important step in the process. While Step One: *Explore* shows you how to get into a reading assignment, Step Two discusses how to understand words you don't know and how to build your vocabulary.

This section of the book contains two chapters on vocabulary to help you better understand your science reading. These chapters can help you read the sciences as well as help you listen, speak, and write with less effort. Chapter 3, the first in this section, discusses scientific language, understanding words in context, proper use of glossaries and indexes, and how scientific words or symbols are used. Chapter 4 gives you methods which can help you improve your vocabulary in general plus the titles of some books on vocabulary improvement.

There are no magic memory devices or short cuts to vocabulary building. Most people with poor vocabularies are poor readers. They don't read enough to *need* a strong vocabulary. If you are a poor reader and you want to be a better one, you must work on vocabulary building, and building a vocabulary at this stage of your education is hard work. You have to start with the basic foundation and work up. Many books, good and bad, have been written about vocabulary building. This book only offers you some blueprints. You'll have to do the building yourself.

3

Understanding Scientific Language

The total picture. This chapter approaches scientific language in three ways. First, it helps you to understand and use the specialized vocabulary of science either by finding the meaning of a word in the context in which it is used or by finding it in a glossary, an index, a dictionary, or an encyclopedia. Second, it helps you recognize words that stand for concepts rather than facts. Third, it introduces you to the use of symbols in scientific writing. Remember that this chapter is only a part of Step Two. Explore it as you were shown in Chapter 2 before reading carefully.

Scientific literacy

Literacy is usually defined as the ability to read and write with a fair amount of proficiency. *Scientific literacy* would be the ability to read and write scientific subject matter. What is your scientific literacy? Test it by defining the following words.

(1) achromatic _____

_____

(2) aerodynamics _____

_____

(3) alkali _____

_____

(4) alloy _____

_____

(5) antibodies _____

_____

(6) biochemistry _____

_____

(7) catalyst _____

_____

(8) cathode _____

(9) cellulose _____

(10) cholesterol _____

(11) chromosomes _____

(12) cretin _____

(13) DNA _____

(14) ecology _____

(15) enzymes _____

(16) fission _____

(17) fusion _____

(18) gestation _____

(19) glucose _____

(20) hemophilia _____

(21) ionosphere _____

(22) micron _____

(23) node _____

(24) pathology _____

(25) plankton _____

How well you did with this list could be relevant to how well you will be able to succeed in your science classes, especially biology and physics. If you felt comfortable with most of these words, your vocabulary-building task will not be as rough as it would be for someone who missed half or more. Check your answers against these:

(1) *Achromatic* means colorless. In optics it means a microscope lens which reflects white light without breaking it up into its component colors; in biology, staining poorly.

(2) *Aerodynamics* is the branch of science which studies the behavior

of air and other gases acting on bodies moving through the air or on fixed bodies in a current of air.

(3) An *alkali* is a soluble base which neutralizes an acid.

(4) *Alloy* is a term used by metallurgists to denote a substance consisting of two or more metallic elements or of a metal and a nonmetallic element.

(5) *Antibodies* are certain chemicals in the blood which neutralize and counteract infectious diseases.

(6) *Biochemistry* is the science which deals with the chemical compounds and processes occurring in plants and animals.

(7) *Catalysts* are chemical substances which speed up or retard chemical reactions while remaining unchanged.

(8) *Cathodes* are negative electrodes. In an electron tube the cathode emits electrons.

(9) *Cellulose* is the substance (identical to starch) which forms the main framework of plant cells.

(10) *Cholesterol* is a fat-like chemical compound that collects in the blood vessels. (Some doctors consider it responsible for high blood pressure.)

(11) *Chromosomes* are strand-like bodies making up all cells in which genes are contained.

(12) A *cretin* is a person suffering from a deficiency of the thyroid gland secretion, usually resulting in dwarfism or idiocy.

(13) *DNA* is deoxyribonucleic acid which is believed to carry all the hereditary traits of a species.

(14) *Ecology* is the investigation of the relationship of animals and plants to their environment.

(15) *Enzymes* are organic catalysts which are responsible for the majority of the chemical changes in living matter such as digestion.

(16) *Fission* in biology is reproduction by the simple division of a cell into two individual cells. In physics, fission is the splitting of an atom into smaller atoms, some of the matter being converted into energy.

(17) *Fusion* is the act or operation of melting or blending together.

(18) *Gestation* is the period of pregnancy.

(19) *Glucose* is the chemical name for a natural sugar found in fruits and in the blood.

(20) *Hemophilia* is a condition, usually hereditary, in which the blood cannot clot.

(21) The *ionosphere* is a region of electrically charged (ionized) air beginning about 25 miles above the surface of the earth.

(22) A *micron* is a unit of length, the one-millionth part of a meter.

(23) A *node* is the joint of a stem (botany) or a swelling like a knot (anatomy and zoology).

(24) *Pathology* is the science of treating diseases, their nature, and causes.

(25) *Plankton* is a term that refers to the tiny animals and plants that float or swim weakly on the ocean's surface.

Since science continues to play such a large part in our everyday lives, it is important that even the man in the street has some acquaintance with the language of science. Often a word you encounter in your science textbooks may seem extremely technical, and its meaning in physics or in biology may be quite different from its everyday meaning. You may feel that there are too many words to learn and that the terminology used by scientists is too complex.

But remember that science attempts to be precise. Scientists use technical words because such a word generally has only one meaning. For instance, the words *aphasia* and *speechlessness* may appear to mean the same thing. But a doctor would never use the word speechlessness as synonymous with aphasia because *speechlessness* implies a temporary inability to talk, usually because of fear or surprise. *Aphasia*, however, is an abnormal loss of speech due to brain damage. The scientist prefers a word that means one thing and one thing only.

There is still another reason for technical terms. It is much easier to use the word *micron* than to say "the one-millionth part of a meter." Or to say, "He has hemophilia," instead of "He has blood that is unable to clot." And it is more simple for a chemist to use the symbol "C_2H_6O" than "two atoms of carbon, six atoms of hydrogen, and one atom of oxygen."

There is, then, a need for scientific terminology and a reason for you to learn it. The remainder of this chapter will show you how to tackle words you don't know as you read your science assignments.

Word context and meanings

In most scientific textbooks, particularly books written for introductory courses, the authors attempt to define the terms they are using within the context of their writing. Notice in this sample passage how the author tries to clarify his terms as he discusses molecular structure.

► All matter (that which has mass and occupies space) is composed of submicroscopic particles, called **molecules**, which are in continuous motion. Such molecules are the smallest subdivision of a substance* which still possesses all of the specific properties or characteristics of that substance. Since these particles are not visible, their motility has been determined by various indirect methods. However, a visible indication that water molecules are moving can be obtained by observing what has been termed **Brownian movement.** If small but visible particles (such as India ink) are suspended in a drop of water and observed through a microscope, these parti-

---

*Substance: a material all samples of which have the same set of properties; it consists of but one kind of molecule.

cles will be seen to "jiggle" about. Their non-directional trembling movement is not a result of their own molecular composition but of the motion of water molecules striking first from one direction and then from another. The unequal collisions push the ink particles first to one side and then to another.[1]

From the beginning the author is defining terms for you. In the first sentence he defines matter by inserting a definition in parentheses "(that which has mass and occupies space)." Then in the same sentence he states that all matter is composed of "submicroscopic particles, called *molecules*, which are in continuous motion." What he has done is define in context two words for you, *matter* and *molecules*.

In his second sentence he elaborates on the word *molecules* and uses the word *substance*. Knowing the word is vague, he footnotes it and gives you the definition of the word as he wants you to understand it. The footnote is used as an aid for the reader and is used instead of parentheses because it is less of an interruption.

Still another term is defined in this paragraph: *Brownian movement*. He mentions the term as a way of visibly observing water molecule movement. There is no reason to be puzzled by the term because he immediately follows through with its definition as well as its purpose.

As an alert reader, you should be able to see the author doing several things for you to make your reading easier. One, he has put the two main terms he wants you to know into bold type: **molecules** and **Brownian movement**. This is a clue to their importance. Second, the author uses parentheses and a footnote to clarify terms that are less important but nonetheless necessary to an understanding of the important terms. Third, he defines words in context through two means. Take a look at the first sentence again. Matter is defined *after* the word is used. The definition of molecules is presented before the word is used. These are all methods widely used in science textbooks to help you understand technical words as they are used in context. Your reading will be easier if you use this knowledge as you read.

Here is another passage from a science textbook. How does it define words in context?

▶   Molecules in turn are composed of **atoms,** the building blocks, which are the smallest particles that will enter into a chemical reaction. Recent evidence indicates that atomic structure is more complicated than had been suspected, but for our purpose we may consider an atom to be made up of a sphere or swarm of **electrons** (negatively charged particles) surrounding a positively charged core.* The posi-

---

[1]Muller, *op. cit.*, pp. 26-27.

   *The term "nucleus" (rather than "core") is used by physicists and chemists, but this might lead to confusion in the mind of a beginning biology student, who is more familiar with a cellular nucleus than with an atomic nucleus.

tive charge is due to **protons** (discrete units of positive charge), but the core also contains particles having no charge at all, the **neutrons**. This central portion contains practically the entire mass of the atom but occupies an extremely tiny portion of the volume; practically all the volume is occupied by electrons. In a neutral atom, the negative charge of the electrons is exactly balanced by the positive charge of the core; the number of electrons is equal to the number of protons. When an electron is removed from a neutral atom, the particle which remains behind is positively charged, or a **positive ion:**

$$Na \rightarrow Na^+ + e^-$$

The electron is shown as e^-. When a neutral atom picks up an electron, it forms a **negative ion:**

$$Cl + e^- \rightarrow Cl^-$$

The symbols Na and Cl refer to sodium and chlorine respectively. Such symbols are the chemists' method of abbreviating the name of an **element,** a substance which cannot be decomposed into simpler substances by ordinary action. Table 3-1 indicates some of the elements which are important in cellular structure and function.[2] ◄

As a means of checking yourself, list at least four ways the author defines words in context in the previous paragraph:

1. _____
2. _____
3. _____
4. _____

The author uses the following aids: (1) he designates the terms he is defining in bold type; (2) he uses parentheses to define terms; (3) he uses a footnote to explain the term as he wants it used; (4) he sometimes gives his definitions *before* the word he is defining appears and sometimes *afterward*; and (5) he defines by using symbols, as in $Na \rightarrow Na^+ + e^-$. In addition, he refers the reader to Table 3-1, which elaborates on his definition of cellular structure.

Naturally, you must learn the terms being defined as you come to them or you will be lost later. If you pay attention to the way the authors of your science textbooks define words in context, you can save yourself many trips to the dictionary or glossary.

---

[2]*Ibid.*, p. 27.

Glossaries and indexes

Before reaching for a dictionary to look up a word you can't define from context, find out whether your textbook has a glossary of terms at the end of each chapter or at the end of the book. (Of course, you probably remember that as part of the exploring technique already mentioned in Step One.)

If the words you are having trouble with are related to the subject you are reading, the author may have defined them for you in the glossary. An author generally knows when a reader might have trouble with a specialized word or term. He will either explain it in context, footnote it, or list it in a glossary.

Another aid that many readers aren't familiar with is the subject index. Pretend for a moment that you are reading your life sciences text and you come to this passage:

► Vegetative reproduction is lacking in human beings and in the animals most familiar to us, the other vertebrates, but some animals do reproduce vegetatively. Such reproduction is not the rule in animals and there are few — perhaps no — animal species in which it is the *sole* means of reproduction. Nevertheless, it does occur in many different kinds of invertebrates and even in tunicates, animals related to the vertebrates. Vegetative reproduction in animals is usually by budding (as in *Hydra*) or by fission (as in planarians), processes not always clearly distinguishable.[3] ◄

You get to the sentence "Vegetative reproduction in animals is usually by budding (as in *Hydra*) . . . ." The name *Hydra* is familiar, though you don't quite remember how it reproduces. Yet it is important that you remember, because it is related to the chapter you are now reading. Here's where the subject index can help you.

If you turned to the index, here's what you would see under *Hydra*[4]:

► *Hydra*, 321, 375, 550; circulatory system in, *307;* digestion in, 290, *291;* gastrulation in, 230; locomotion in, 402, *402;* nerve net in, *376,* 402; photosynthetic protists in cells of, *650;* radial symmetry in, 572; reproduction in, 246, *246,* 248, 265 ◄

The quantity of page number listings may overwhelm you at first, but for your purpose you don't need to read all the references. Notice there is a listing "reproduction in, 246, *246,* 248, 265." These would be the best pages to start with.

Since there are three listings here, your safest bet is to check the first

---

[3]Simpson and Beck, *op. cit.*, p. 265.
[4]*Ibid.*, p. 859.

page listed. Most of the time, though not always, the initial listing will be the place where the most was said about the subject. Once you turn to that page, don't try to read all of the page. Skim over it, letting your eyes search out the key words, in this case *Hydra* and *vegetative reproduction*. Once you find these terms being used, read carefully. Ignore everything but passages dealing with what you are looking for. All you want is something that may help you understand the term as it is being used in your reading assignment.

So you can follow through on this example, here is page 246 as it appears in the textbook. For practice, see how quickly you can find out how Hydra reproduces.

Figure 3.1. Vegetative reproduction in *Hydra*, an animal. A bud in *Hydra* is an evagination of the polyp wall containing both ectoderm and endoderm tissue layers. It develops tentacles (barely visible in the photo) and a mouth. Eventually, severing itself completely from the parent, it becomes a new individual.

▶   Quite a few animals, of which *Hydra* is an example (Figure 3.1), reproduce vegetatively by *budding.* Many plants develop special *organs of vegetative reproduction.* Some of these are surely familiar to you: the tubers of potatoes, the bulbs of onions or tulips, the bulb-like organs of gladioli, the runners of strawberries, and the runner-like underground structures of many grasses. Many different parts and processes may be involved in vegetative reproduction, but the principle is always the same and is simple: a part of the parental organism, genetically identical with its other parts, develops into a separate organism.

The other usual form of asexual reproduction is by *spores*, plant reproductive cells each of which develops into a separate organism without fertilization.

The essential feature of sexual reproduction is the fusion of two nuclei within a single cell, which develops into a separate organism. You will recall from Chapter 5 that the specialized sexual reproductive cells of plants and animals are gametes and that they usually are of two kinds: smaller, more mobile male gametes, or sperms, and larger, more passive female gametes, or eggs. The union of male and female gametes is fertilization, and the resulting single cell is a zygote. In some protists and lower plants, the two cells whose nuclei fuse are not visibly different from each other or from ordinary cells (or, in protists, whole organisms) of the species. The male and female are not distinguishable, and the lack of apparent specialization for reproduction may make the term "gamete" seem inappropriate. Nevertheless, such cells have gone through meiosis and are fully comparable with gametes in this preparation for fusion by reduction of chromosome number.*

Modes of achieving sexual reproduction have become amazingly diverse in plants and animals. The gametes have acquired numerous different characteristics in different groups. Organs associated with their production, with fertilization, and with subsequent development of the offspring have become extremely specialized and have also taken innumerable different forms. Nevertheless, sexual reproduction is essentially the same and has the same evolutionary and biological significance whether it occurs in paramecia, roses, or humans. The basic phenomenon is that half of the chromosomes from each of two individuals have been united in a single new individual.[5] ◄

You should be able to understand quickly what vegetative reproduction is after reading the opening paragraph in the first column and looking at Figure 3.1. In fact, your best and simplest definition is found in the last sentence of the first paragraph:

Many different parts and processes may be involved in vegetative reproduction, but the principle is always the same and is simple: a part of the parental organism, genetically identical with its other parts, develops into a separate organism.*

Now that you understand this, you are ready to return to your reading assignment and continue reading with better comprehension than if you had skipped over the terms. However, too many trips back to previously read assignments via the index would indicate a poor initial reading of the assigned pages. If you must, take the time to reread assignments but you should find such trips less necessary the more you put the steps in this book to work for you.

---

*Some biologists object to applying the term "fertilization" to fusion of nuclei in protists and do not consider this as sexual reproduction. They call passage of the nucleus, only, from one individual to another "conjugation," and fusion of two individuals, both nuclei and cytoplasm, "syngamy." Nevertheless, in essence and real biological significance conjugation or syngamy in protists and fertilization in multicellular organisms are fundamentally the same. In both, haploid cells (or their nuclei) fuse and produce a new diploid individual. It is not confusing two different things but recognizing their essential equivalence when the same terms are applied to the process in protists and in other organisms.
[5]*Ibid.*, p. 246.

Last resort: The dictionary or encyclopedia

It's up to you to learn the important terms as you come to them in your reading. Imagine for a moment now that the passage you just read is part of an assignment you are reading for the first time: "In both, haploid cells (or their nuclei) fuse and produce a new diploid individual." This sentence may stop you because you can't understand *haploid* or *diploid* from their contextual usage. You check the glossary, but the words aren't defined there. If there is no helpful index listing, you must now go beyond the textbook itself.

This means going to the dictionary or encyclopedia. Of course, you don't *have* to learn what *haploid* and *diploid* mean. After all, if you have a poor vocabulary and you look up every word you don't know, you can waste a lot of time. But reading without understanding isn't a very good use of time either.

If you have been dodging the problem of poor vocabulary in the past, this is a good time to face it. While it would be preposterous to stop and look up every word you don't know, you do have to begin somewhere. At least look up the words which keep you from getting the main point of the passage. Many reading experts agree that if you read very much, a larger vocabulary comes almost automatically as you see words used in context. But since not all words can be understood from context, trips to the dictionary or encyclopedia are often necessary and helpful.

Here's what you might find if you decided to look up the word *haploid* in a scientific encyclopedia:

▶   *Haploid.* The single, or *n*, chromosome number of organisms in which there is only one kind of each chromosome in a cell, in contrast to the diploid, double, or 2*n*, chromosome number in which there are two of each kind of chromosome in a cell. The haploid number of chromosomes is found in cells after **meiosis** and before fertilization restores the diploid number. In most animals only the gametes are haploid, but in many plants a rather large mass of haploid tissue is formed after meiosis and before gametes are formed. (See **Alternation of Generations.**) The bacteria, many of the molds, and many of the algae have haploid cells and become diploid only temporarily when there is some form of sexual union. Haploid cells and tissues express all of the genes in the cells because there are no dominant genes to repress the expression of recessive genes.[6] ◀

With the aid of the definition you can almost visualize what is happening when haploid cells "fuse and produce a new diploid individual."

If you haven't yet spent a little time exploring a science dictionary according to the methods discussed in Step One, try it.

Concepts

A *concept* in science is an idea that exists as a generalized idea based on knowledge to explain a phenomenon. Scientists use the process of analysis to develop certain concepts to help determine the why's and how's. For example, in physics the conceptual unit is the atom with its electrons, protons, and other particles; in biology, the cell.

Scientists approach their subject by taking facts and generalizing about them. Here is what one scientist has to say about science and concepts:

▶   Although facts are ultimate, their significance may alter. Facts are not phenomena; they are *descriptions* of phenomena. They are abstractions from the phenomena. They depend upon the *concepts*, the *ideas*, with which one approaches the phenomena. For example, the description of falling bodies is made in terms of certain concepts, such as time, distance, speed, and so on. With different concepts, different facts are obtained. Facts are ultimate, but only in the sense that in terms of a given set of concepts, certain things can be described as happening. What we choose to describe and the terms in which we describe it are *not* in the phenomena. The development of science is in a large measure the development of concepts.[7] ◀

If then, "the development of science is in a large measure the development of concepts," it would be well for you to be able to identify scientific concepts.

Here is a passage from a science text. As you read it, try to identify the major words or terms being used as concepts.

▶   A common form of energy, and perhaps the easiest to understand, is the energy of lifted bodies. If we lift a body of 10 pounds to a height of 6 feet from the floor, we do 60 foot-pounds of work. We have spent 60 foot-pounds of energy. But now a curious thing happens. The lifted body now has energy, because it can now do work. For example, the lifted body can be attached to a pulley or to a lever, and on falling back to the floor it can lift an equal weight to the same height, or half of the weight to twice the height. By a different arrangement the lifted body can be made to drag a weight across the floor, sweep the floor, open the door, and so on. In other words, the lifted body now

---

[7]Ashford, *op. cit.*, p. 10.

has energy because it can do work; that is, it can exert a *force* for a *distance.*[8] ◄

The following is a list of words taken from the sample paragraph. Place a C in front of each word that you think is a concept.

_____1. energy   _____4. lifted
_____2. bodies   _____5. pulley
_____3. work   _____6. force

All but items 2 and 5 are concepts. Energy, work, lifting, and force are all concepts. You can't touch them and they have no form or boundaries. But they are part of the sort of vocabulary used frequently by scientists, and they are just as "real," in a scientific sense, as facts.

Symbols

A *scientific symbol* is an abbreviation that represents a word or a concept. Recognizing symbols is not new or difficult for you. These words you are reading are symbols which represent the sounds we make when we talk. You learned long ago what $+$, $-$, $\times$, and $\div$ mean. They too are symbols for words—add, subtract, multiply, and divide. Science simply uses more sophisticated or elaborate symbols. In science classes you are expected to deal with symbols such as 10^{-6}; μ; or 1 cm $= 0.3937$ in.; or to understand that the following symbol represents a Cytosine base.

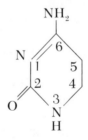

Here is a typical passage from a biology textbook which discusses some compounds of biological importance. Notice the heavy use of symbols.

► *Carbohydrates.*

The name implies that carbon has been hydrated—that is, has had water compounded with it. From a strictly quantitative standpoint there is something to be said for this: glucose, $C_6H_{12}O_6$, can be rewritten $(CH_2O)_6$. The $1:2:1$ ratio of $C:H:O$ in this compound *approximately* obtains in sucrose, $C_{12}H_{22}O_{11}$; in lactose and maltose, also $C_{12}H_{22}O_{11}$; and in raffinose, $C_{18}H_{32}O_{16}$. Glucose is called a "monosaccharide" and sucrose a "disaccharide." These substances are interconvertible by reactions that add (**hydrolysis**) or remove

⁸*Ibid.*, p. 85.

(**condensation**) a molecule of water, thus:

$$C_{12}H_{22}O_{11} + H_2O \xrightarrow{\text{(hydrolysis)}} 2C_6H_{12}O_6; \qquad (9)$$

$$C_{12}H_{22}O_{11} + H_2O \xleftarrow{\text{(condensation)}} 2C_6H_{12}O_6. \qquad (10)$$

The process of condensation can be performed repeatedly to produce polysaccharides (etymologically, "many sugars"). Glycogen, or "animal starch," is a polysaccharide that serves for the chemical storage of energy in animal livers and muscles. The true starches serve the same function in plants; they result from the condensation of many simple sugars. Still more condensed molecules are the celluloses, insoluble compounds that are important constituents of the cell wall of plants.[9] ◀

Also notice that in most cases the meaning of the symbol is given immediately; for example, ". . . and in raffinose, $C_{18}N_{32}O_{16}$." If these seem to be important symbols, it would be a good idea to learn them immediately.

Most textbooks will have appendixes with charts and diagrams for easy reference when you run across symbols you don't remember or know. But if your textbook doesn't, you might wish to obtain a copy of William S. Spector's (ed.) *Handbook of Biological Data* (W. B. Saunders Company) or *Lange's Handbook of Chemistry* (Handbook Publishers). Both of these works contain tables and charts, including the Periodic System, the Metric System, Astronomical Values, miscellaneous mathematical formulas, formulas for organic compounds, and chromosome counts of various species.

SUMMARY

This chapter suggests that the mastery of vocabulary is best achieved by learning words as you come to them in your reading. When you have difficulty with a word in your science textbooks, try these steps:
1. Try to understand the word as it is used in context.
2. If it is impossible to gather meaning from the context, check the footnotes, glossary, or index. If the index refers you to pages on which the word is mentioned, skim through those pages looking for its definition.
3. If you can't find a definition of the term within the textbook, go to the dictionary (preferably to a scientific dictionary or encyclopedia).
4. Once you have found definitions for all the words you don't know or can't define from the context, return to the reading assignment and reread it. As you read, keep in mind the special meanings of the words.

Make certain that you thoroughly understand this phase of Step Two before going on to Chapter 4. You may wish to do the practice exercises on pages 187–195.

---

[9]Hardin, *op. cit.*, p. 71.

4

Building Your Vocabulary

The total picture. When you explore this chapter, remember that it is still part of Step Two: *Check the Vocabulary.* Chapter 3 showed you ways to find the meanings of words in your science readings. This chapter presents three methods, any or all of which you may wish to use for building not only your science vocabulary but your general reading vocabulary.

1. Learning important key roots and affixes contained in many words.
2. Making and using personalized vocabulary cards.
3. Using helpful books on vocabulary building.

Now explore this chapter. Then read carefully, looking for a method that may work for you. You may want to combine methods or devise one of your own.

Ways to build your vocabulary

To build your vocabulary, you can use several methods. Each of them is effective for some people. It's a matter of deciding what system seems best for you and then working at it. And there is no getting around the work part. Building up your vocabulary is like building up your muscles, no one can do your exercises for you.

Three ways of building your vocabulary are presented here. Look them over and see which you prefer. Then put the method to work.

Method One: Key roots and affixes

Are you familiar with the following words?

autograph	phonograph
biography	photograph
geography	telegraph
mimeograph	graphite
paragraph	graphic

There probably isn't any word on this list that you don't already know.

Why do you suppose they all contain the Greek root *graph*? Do you know why we call the lead in pencils graphite? Do you know why an autograph is called that? The Greek root *graph* means "to write, draw, or record." The definition of each of the words above has something to do with writing, drawing, or recording.

Take the word *autograph. Auto*, in Greek, means "self"; hence *autograph* refers to self-writing, or one's own writing, usually one's name as we use the word today. The word *biography* includes the Greek root *bio*, meaning "life"; hence *biography* refers to life record, or a written record of someone's life. *Geo* means "earth"; hence *geography* refers to earth record, or writings about the earth.

If you bothered to look up each word in the group above, you would find that they all come from Greek word sources. Many words in the English language can be traced back to Greek and Latin. In fact, a great many of the scientific and medical terms used today are derived from these two languages. Since this is so, one of the best ways to improve your vocabulary is to study roots and affixes (affixes include both prefixes and suffixes) from these two major sources.

Lists of some of the more important Greek and Latin roots and affixes are given here for your study. Some of the spellings may be changed slightly from the original because these are the forms as we use them today. You may wish to look each one up in a dictionary to see how many words are built on it (if so, use a good dictionary). Or you may wish to commit them to memory. The advantage of learning these word parts is that whenever you run across a new word containing these parts, you can usually unlock its meaning without a trip to the dictionary. At any rate, a student at your educational level should know these words and their parts. In each of the blank spaces, you write a word you know that contains the affix given in the first column.

Greek word roots and affixes

Root or affix	Meaning	Word using root or affix	Your word
acou, acu	to hear	acoustics	_____
auto	self	automatic	_____
amphi	on both sides	amphitheater	_____
anti	against, opposite	antibiotic	_____
arthr	joint	arthritis	_____
anthro, anthrop	man, mankind	philanthropy	_____
biblio	book	bibliography	_____
bio	life	biology	_____
cardi	heart	cardiac	_____

cephal	head	cephalopod	_____
chlor	green	chlorophyll	_____
chron	time	chronological	_____
cyt	cell	cytology	_____
dia	across, through	diameter	_____
epi	upon	epidemic	_____
gen	kinds, race, origin	genealogy	_____
geo	earth	geology	_____
graph	write, record	graphite	_____
hedron	solid figure with many faces	octohedron	_____
helio	sun	heliotherapy	_____
hemo	blood	hemophile	_____
hetero	mixed	heterogeneous	_____
homo	same, alike	homogeneous	_____
hydro	water	hydrolysis	_____
itis	inflammation of	tonsillitis	_____
log(y)	study of	astrology	_____
macro	large	macroscopic	_____
mania	craze for	maniac	_____
meter	measure	chronometer	_____
micro	small	microscope	_____
mono	one	monopoly	_____
neuro	nerve	neurotic	_____
octo	eight	octopus	_____
ost; osteo	bone	osteopath	_____
para	beside, aside from	parameter	_____
patho	disease of	pathology	_____
peri	around	periscope	_____
phil	love	bibliophile	_____
phobos	fear	phobia	_____
phon	sound	phonograph	_____
poly	many	polygamy	_____
psyche	mind, soul	psychology	_____
scope	examine	stethoscope	_____
som, somat	body	chromosome	_____
syn	together	synchronize	_____
tach, tachy	swift, speed	tachometer	_____
tele	far, distance	telephone	_____
thera	to nurse	therapy	_____
zoo	animals	zoo	_____

To make certain that you understand how the above list of Greek word parts can be helpful to you, test yourself on the following list. Below are ten words that use the Greek roots and affixes in the list above. Using the list, divide each word into its parts. For example: *perimeter: peri* = around, *meter* = measure. Then write what you think is the correct definition for the word. When you are finished, look up each word in the dictionary and see how close your definition comes to it.

1. psychotherapy
2. hemophile
3. zoology
4. geology
5. polyphony
6. anthropology
7. arthritis
8. neuropathy
9. heliotherapy
10. osteopath

Latin word roots and affixes

Root or affix	Meaning	Word using root or affix	Your word
ante	before	antecedent	_____
aqua	water	aqualung	_____
audio	hear	audiometer	_____
aur	ear	aural	_____
bene	well	benefit	_____
cap, cip, cept	take	capacious, capacity	_____
carn	flesh	carnivorous	_____
circum	around	circumference	_____
cord	heart	cordial	_____
corpus	body	corpse	_____
credo	belief	incredulous	_____
digit	finger; toe	digital	_____
dis	not; apart	disappear	_____
dominus	lord	dominate	_____
dorm	sleep	dormant	_____
duc, duct	lead	conductor	_____
ego	I, self	ego	_____
ex	out	exit	_____
frater	brother	fraternize	_____
in	not	incredible	_____
inter	between	interact	_____
locus	place	locality	_____
mitto, mit	send	transmit	_____
mortis, mort	death	mortality	_____
ocul	eye	oculist	_____

pater	father	paternal	_____
ped	foot	octoped	_____
port	carry	porter, transport	_____
post	after	posticous	_____
pre	before	premedical	_____
pro	before	project, procambium	_____
sanguin, sangui	blood	consanguinity	_____
scribe	write	transcribe	_____
solus	alone	solo	_____
somn	sleep	insomnia	_____
son	sound	ultrasonic	_____
subter	under, secret	subterranean	_____
trans	across	transport	_____
utilis	useful	utility	_____
video	see	video	_____

Now see if you can use the guide to Latin roots and affixes to find the parts of the following words. Follow the same directions as in the last vocabulary check. Then look up each word in the dictionary and see how close the meaning of the combined parts is to the dictionary definition. (Example: *transport*: *trans* = across; *port* = carry.)

1. postmortem
2. circumscribe
3. subsonic
4. solar
5. inscribe
6. inaudible
7. proscribe
8. corporal
9. captivate
10. egocentric

Here are a few other roots, from both Greek and Latin, that are frequently found in words used in the sciences as well as your general reading.

Root or affix	Meaning	Word using root or affix	Your word
a-, an-	without	apathy	_____
aesth, esth	feeling, perception	aesthetic, esthetic	_____
caco	bad	cacophony	_____
cosm	order, world	cosmos	_____
eu	good	euphony	_____
etym	true meaning	etymology	_____
gnos	to know	agnostic	_____
gon	angle	octagon	_____

hepta	seven	heptagon	_____
hexa	six	hexameter	_____
ideo	idea	ideology	_____
latry	worship	heliolatry	_____
log	idea; word; reason	biology	_____
path	feeling	apathetic	_____
syn, sym	together	symphony	_____
theo	god	theology	_____
verb	word	verbal	_____
virtu	skill	virtuoso	_____

This, of course, is just a short list of words you will encounter in your reading of science and other subjects. Learn them and their roots and you will save yourself many trips to the dictionary.

Method Two: Personalized vocabulary cards

You have probably seen boxed sets of vocabulary cards for foreign languages as well as for English. They usually have a word on one side and its definition on the other. These ready-made cards can be helpful, but there may be many words on the cards that you already know and some that you will probably never see or hear. You can easily make your own, however, using words you want to learn.

In your reading or in conversation, you often meet a word that seems familiar; you know that you've seen or heard it before but you're not sure of its meaning. That word belongs in your permanent vocabulary. Print the word on a 3 × 5 card in ink so that after much use it will still be legible. Underneath the word print its phonetic spelling as given in the dictionary, unless you already know how to pronounce the word. The front side of the card should look like this:

Perspicuous

(pĕr - spik'ū -əs)

If you do not know how to interpret phonetic symbols, turn to the pronunciation guide in your dictionary. There you will usually find enough examples of words you already know how to pronounce to figure out how to pronounce any word in the dictionary. You should realize, however, that dictionaries don't always agree on which pronunciation is preferable. Remember that a dictionary is not a rule book but simply a record of how most people say and use words. Listen for the word and practice using it; in a short while you should feel comfortable in your pronunciation of it.

On the back of the card, put as much information as you need to help you learn the words. Besides the definition, it's a good idea to include a synonym (a word that has a similar meaning) which you already know. Also include an antonym (a word that has an opposite meaning). It helps, too, to write a sentence using the word you're learning. This forces you to test the word out to see if you really know its meaning well enough to use it. The back of the card might look something like this:

Perspicuous
Definition: plain to understand,
            not obscure
Synonym: Clear
Antonym: obscure
The teacher's lecture was
perspicuous.

Why all this bother? Why not write only the definition? If you can associate the word you want to learn with words that you already know, you will be more likely to remember the word's meaning and recognize it when you see it or hear it used. Writing the sentence will help you learn how to use the word in your own writing and speech. The best way to know words is in context, as mentioned in Chapter 3, and a sentence on the card gives you a context. A word really doesn't mean anything until someone uses it.

"Why the cards in the first place?" The answer lies in what you do with the cards after you have made them. Just memorizing words is no way to build a lasting vocabulary. All of the words you use in everyday conversation and reading are part of your verbal arsenal. You respond to them without stopping to think about their meaning. You have used them so often that they come naturally to you. Vocabulary cards will help you add new words to your arsenal. The following paragraphs will help you use vocabulary cards to your best advantage.

1. Once you have a stack of about fifteen to twenty cards, keep them mixed up, in no particular order. Spend about ten minutes each day pronouncing the words on the front of your cards and then recalling each word's meaning. Don't use the information on the back of the card unless you have to.

2. Carry a small stack of cards around with you in your pocket or purse. When you have some spare time—between classes, on a bus, waiting for a lecture to start—practice running through your cards. The more you do this, the sooner you will be sure of the new words. The idea is to overlearn them so you don't have to stop and think what each word means.

3. As the weeks go by and you accumulate fifty to a hundred cards, put aside the cards for words that you feel you know very well and work with the others, adding new words as you find or need them. At a later date, review the cards you put aside and see if you still remember them. If there are some you aren't certain about, put them back into your active stack of cards.

4. Don't attempt to make a card for every word that you don't know. Be selective, especially at the beginning. Make cards only for words that you encounter more than once and that you think are useful.

5. You may wish to have separate stacks of vocabulary cards, each stack dealing with a different subject. If, at present, your major vocabulary concern is biology, start accumulating biology words from your text and practicing with them. You might be surprised at how this method can help you not only with your reading assignments in the course, but with tests as well.

All this may seem like too much work. Perhaps it's not the method for you. But it has worked well for many students. Usually when you keep cards as a class requirement, you have no trouble with them because you have an opportunity for the instructor to check them for accuracy and to listen to you pronounce them. But remember that in this method of building your own vocabulary, you are the teacher and you have to grade yourself.

Method Three: Studying books on vocabulary building

There are many books devoted entirely to the building of vocabulary. As you broaden your interest in vocabulary development, you may wish to read one or more of them. Here are some books that go into great detail about words and their meanings.

Ayers, Donald M. *English Words from Latin and Greek Elements.*
The University of Arizona Press, 1965.

All the words in this book, as the title indicates, are based on Latin and Greek elements. It is a very thorough book which provides roots and affixes to learn, with explanations of their meaning and examples of words containing these bases. There are also exercises for checking your progress. In addition to separating the Latin and Greek bases, the author also gives lists of sea terms, military terms, literary terms, and so on. If you like Method One in this chapter, you'll like this book.

Brown, James I. *Programmed Vocabulary.*
Appleton-Century-Crofts, 1964.

This book is a bit different from the conventional book in that it is programmed. It is almost impossible to be thinking about something else while you read it because you must answer questions as you read. If you make a wrong answer, you are corrected immediately. Its drills are based on fourteen master words whose roots and affixes are keys to over 14,000 words. This book is based on the concept of self-education.

Davis, Nancy. *Vocabulary Improvement.*
McGraw-Hill, 1967.

This is another programmed text. You progress at your own rate through this book. The vocabulary taught in this text is not technical or specialized but instead provides a program for developing a good general vocabulary. It is divided into five units: (1) Most Commonly Used Prefixes and Roots; (2) More Latin and Greek; (3) Refresher: Counting and Suffixes; (4) Vocabulary in Context; and (5) What to Do Next.

Didas, Mary. *Words and Ideas.*
College Entrance Publications Corporation, 1959.

This book presents short reading selections from a variety of authors, including Washington Irving, Edgar Allen Poe, and Rachel Carson. Both comprehension questions and vocabulary drills are given for each selection. The drills deal with synonyms, antonyms, and pairs of words that you must match with other paired words. For example, *grass: verdant* would be matched with *sky: blue.* Each chapter has an alphabetical list with definitions of the words that appear in the reading selection or drills.

Greene, Amsel. *Word Clues.*
Harper & Row, 1962.

There are two sections in this book: one on Greek roots and the other on Latin roots. In each section, the lessons give you some roots and affixes to learn. Then you are given fifteen words that use these roots. By associating the roots you've learned with the fifteen words in the drill, you figure out the meanings of the words without referring to a dictionary. After the first four lessons, you are given a drill of over a hundred words whose meanings you can determine by using what you have learned in the previous four lessons. An excellent book if you like Method One in this text.

Funk, Wilfred, and Norman Lewis. *30 Days to a More Powerful Vocabulary.*

Washington Square Press, 1949.

    This book requires you to spend about 15 minutes each day for a period of 30 days on vocabulary building. Each chapter is devoted to a specific type of vocabulary drill, with constant review of the words found in previous chapters. Most of the words are very practical ones that you should have in your general vocabulary.

Miller, Ward. *Word Wealth.*

Henry Holt and Company, 1958.

    Each unit in this book is built on a group of words that are members of a "family." For instance, under the family *personalities* the following words are discussed: *huckster, friar, mendicant, pauper, stowaway, vagabond, waif, urchin,* and *stripling.* The words are defined and used with examples.

Norwood, J. E. *Concerning Words and Phrasing.*

Prentice-Hall, 1960.

    The first chapter of this book introduces you to the dictionary. Several chapters are devoted to affixes, defining them and giving you drills in their use. The book then deals with *stems,* or the combination of letters that is the root or key part of a word. For example, what is the key part of the words *interlude, allude,* and *delude?*

Roberts, Clyde. *Word Attack.*

Harcourt, Brace & World, 1956.

    The drills in vocabulary cover words in context; sounds that aid spelling and pronunciation; structural aids dealing with syllables, prefixes, and suffixes; visual recognition of words by their configuration; and use of the dictionary.

Taylor, Stanford, et al. *Word Clue Books, J,K,L,N.* Educational Development Laboratories, 1963.

    Each of the four books contains three hundred words at a particular level of difficulty, beginning with tenth grade. They are programmed books offering you work that you can check yourself. Each word is used in context, so that you can learn not only its definition but also how to use it appropriately.

    The books listed next are not vocabulary books, but they are science dictionaries and might be of interest to you if your textbook does not have a glossary or if you are required to do much outside scientific reading.

Foster, John, Jr. *Science Writers Guide.*

Columbia University Press, 1963.

    This is not a science dictionary *per se,* but the major part of the book alphabetically lists definitions of contemporary scientific terms. It also has a section on medical terms.

Gaynor, Frank. *Concise Dictionary of Science.*

Littlefield, Adams & Company, 1964.

While the numerous definitions are quite short, this is an accurate and rather comprehensive volume, handy to have around for quick reference.

Speck, G. E. and Bernard Jaffee. *A Dictionary of Science Terms.*
Hawthorn Books, Inc., 1965.

There are over 3000 entries in this volume and 136 illustrations. It reads like an encyclopedic dictionary and contains many tables and charts outlining atomic and fundamental constants, planetary data, atomic elements, and the like.

Now—a word of caution: spending money for a book may make you feel better, but it won't automatically build your vocabulary. There's no magic in vocabulary books. If you are reading this book on your own, and you feel you need more help than this chapter gives you, you may want to enroll in a reading or vocabulary class. However, your problems with words are your own, and the only answer, finally, is to find your own method and work at it.

SUMMARY

Vocabulary is essential to good reading. Before you can understand what you read, you obviously have to understand the words. A course or a self-help book in vocabulary is, at best, merely a device. There is no single best way to build vocabulary. You have to find your own best method by trying various approaches. This chapter has called your attention to three such methods: (1) studying roots and affixes; (2) making vocabulary cards and using them; (3) using vocabulary-building books.

This chapter concludes Step Two: *Check the Vocabulary.* Before going on to the next step, pause and reflect on the two chapters in this step. Each one deals with a different aspect of vocabulary. You may wish to turn now to the vocabulary exercises on pages 197–203 in the practice section and complete any or all of them before beginning Step Three.

THREE

Analyze for Comprehension

"Why do instructors always want you to analyze everything you read? Why can't you just read something without having to pick it apart?"

Sound familiar? It's the common complaint of many readers—usually poor readers. A good reader knows that analysis of a book does not mean picking it apart but simply close and careful reading. In learning to analyze you are learning to comprehend what you read. Analysis, then, is meant to liven up reading and make it more enjoyable.

In Step One: *Explore*, you learned to familiarize yourself with what you are going to read before reading it carefully. You learned to prepare yourself for close reading. In Step Two: *Check the Vocabulary*, you learned how to deal with words as they are used in the sciences, as well as how to learn words you don't know. Now you are ready to put these two steps together and learn how to thoroughly understand what you read.

The next five chapters make up Step Three: *Analyze for Comprehension*. Each chapter deals with one type of writing pattern commonly found in science textbooks. Examples of each of these patterns have been taken from actual science textbooks and explicated for you so that when you read your assignments and encounter these patterns, your reading will be easier and your comprehension better.

Research has shown that the most common writing patterns found in science textbooks are the following: (1) the classification pattern in which things (objects, plants, materials) are classified under a common heading with subdivisions; (2) the process-description pattern which explains how something works; (3) the experiment-instructions pattern, in which an experiment must be carried out exactly as prescribed with observations and explanations of what happens; (4) the factual-statement pattern; (5) the problem-solving pattern, in which a question has been answered through a series of experiments which are described; and (6) a combination of patterns in which all of the above-mentioned patterns appear along with charts, tables, and mathematical formulas. Knowledge of these patterns makes it easier for you to adjust your reading skills to each pattern for proper interpretation. Step Three shows you how to do this.

As you read the chapters in this third step, use what you have learned in the previous steps.

5

Analyzing the Classification Pattern

The total picture. As you were told in the Introduction of this book, a good student adjusts his reading skills and approach to fit his purpose and the type of reading material. This chapter is concerned with the reading skills needed for analyzing the classification pattern of writing found frequently in science textbooks. The classification pattern is used to group and subgroup various things, objects, or areas. Learn to recognize this pattern of writing so that you can easily identify the major and minor points being made. Explore this chapter before reading closely.

The classification pattern

The classification pattern of writing is found very frequently in all types of science textbooks. It is especially important in nonpredictive sciences, such as biology and geology. And because it *is* a pattern, you can use it to remember a large number of small pieces of information. It is not a difficult pattern to recognize, nor is it unfamiliar to you. For instance, if you were told to classify the following automobiles, how would you do it?

Chevrolet Impala	Toyota Corolla
Volvo 144	Ford Galaxie
Volkswagen	Mustang
Corvette	MGB
Rolls-Royce Silver Shadow	Dodge Charger

In the space below, classify the above cars.

How you classified the cars depends on what major point you are trying to make about them. If you wanted to show which cars were foreign-made and which were American-made, you might have done this:

American-Made	Foreign-Made
Chevrolet Impala	Volvo 144
Corvette	Volkswagen
Ford Galaxie	Rolls-Royce Silver Shadow
Mustang	Toyota Corolla
Dodge Charger	MGB

Or your main point in classification may be to compare size, in which case you might have done something like this:

Large	Compact	Small
Chevrolet Impala	Corvette	Toyota Corolla
Ford Galaxie	Mustang	Volkswagen
Rolls-Royce Silver Shadow	Volvo 144	MGB
Dodge Charger		

Or you might have used a much more elaborate method:

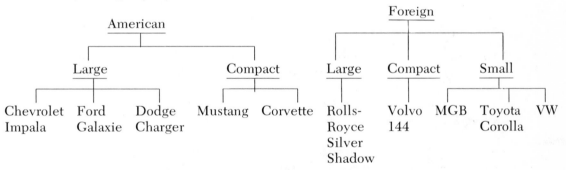

Since two of these cars, the MGB and the Corvette, are sports cars, you could have made the breakdown even more elaborate. Whatever method of classification you used, you probably had a major heading, which represented the main point you were making about the cars, and then subdivisions for the minor points.

Here is a rather typical passage from a geology textbook. Notice how the author uses the classification pattern in his writing, as well as a classification table:

►   North American and British geologists favor the terms Quaternary and Tertiary as Cenozoic subdivisions. European and Russian geologists are inclined to prefer **Neogene** and **Paleogene**. The important mountain-building activity that created the Alps culminated in the middle Tertiary, and this event naturally serves as a guidepost in Old World classifications. The term **Nummulitic Period** is also used in Europe for the combined **Paleocene, Eocene,** and **Oligocene** Epochs in recognition that nummulites — large, disc-shaped fossil protozoans — are common in this interval. We cannot predict which of the proposed terms will be adopted and found best suited for world-wide use.[1] ◄

Cenozoic Era

Classification Used in This Book			Alternative Classification
Quaternary Period	{Recent Epoch	2 million	
	Pleistocene Epoch}	years	Neogene Period
Tertiary Period	Pliocene Epoch	11 m. y.	
	Miocene Epoch	12 m. y.	
	Oligocene Epoch	11 m. y.	
	Eocene Epoch	22 m. y.	Paleogene Period
	Paleocene Epoch	5 m. y.	

The table makes it easy for you to interpret the author's use of terms and the ones he feels are most important. He even uses the words *classification* and *subdivision*; these are clues to the major and minor points. Here you know that the two terms to be subdivided into other parts are quaternary and tertiary periods.

Look now at another pattern of classification. This one comes from an introductory biology textbook. There is no table to help you with this one.

►   All the Ornithischia were primarily herbivorous, but in other respects they became even more diverse than the Saurischia. There were four main groups: the plated dinosaurs, *Stegosaurus* and its relatives, quadrupeds with rows of bony plates down the back; the armored dinosaurs such as *Ankylosaurus*, animated four-footed tanks almost completely enclosed in a bony carapace; the duck-billed dinosaurs, including *Anatosaurus*, mostly bipedal, many of them strong swimmers and more or less amphibious in habits; and the frilled dinosaurs, typified by *Triceratops*, quadrupeds with a bony, frill-like extension of skull bones over the neck and in the more advanced forms usually also with horns. Restorations of all the genera of dinosaurs named as examples are pictured in Fig. 30 – 10, and the skeleton

[1]William Lee Stokes, *Essentials of Earth History: An Introduction to Historical Geology*, 2nd Edition, © 1966. Reprinted by permission of Prentice-Hall, Inc., Englewood Cliffs, New Jersey.

of *Tyrannosaurus* is shown in Fig. 30–11. About 250 genera in all are known, and they have been found on every continent except Antarctica. The richest known deposits are, however, in North America, and our seven examples are all American forms.[2] ◄

In the space below, classify the terms used in the above passage by writing in the names in the appropriate blanks.

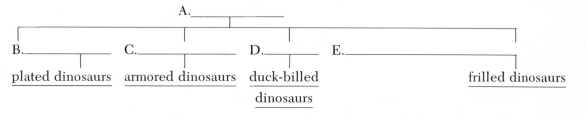

Compare your answers with these: A. Ornithischia; B. Stegosaurus; C. Ankylosaurus; D. Anatosaurus; E. Triceratops. Basically, this passage is discussing the herbivorous (plant-eating) Ornithischia, of which there were four main groups as outlined above. The author, in addition to giving you their names, describes them for you so that you can mentally visualize them. But even more important, he refers you to two figures (Fig. 30–10 and Fig. 30–11). These figures are not reproduced for you here, but if this were a passage from an actual reading assignment, you would use the pictures to help you see the differences. It is often important to interrupt your reading in science books and refer to the charts or pictures provided. They can be a powerful aid to understanding what you are reading.

Structural classification pattern

In the previous examples you were shown how writers use the classification pattern to explain or examine things such as geological periods or the different types of dinosaurs. This same pattern is used to show the structure of things. Here is a sample passage from a beginning botany text using the structural classification pattern to describe plant leaves.

► Although tremendous variations occur in the size and shape of leaves, certain basic structures are distinguishable (Figure 5.1). The **petiole** (or leaf stalk) is a continuation of the stem and contains vascular tissue which is continuous from that of the stem proper to the rest of the leaf. The **blade** is the flattened, expanded portion of the leaf and is usually green in color, due to the presence of many chloroplast-containing cells. Some leaf blades are needle-like, as in

[2]Simpson and Beck, *op. cit.*, pp. 727–728.

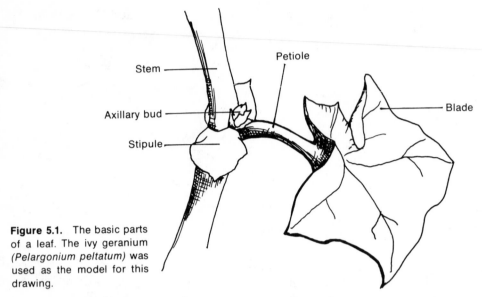

Figure 5.1. The basic parts of a leaf. The ivy geranium *(Pelargonium peltatum)* was used as the model for this drawing.

pine *(Pinus)*, or scale-like, as in cypress *(Cupressus* spp.). Most of the food manufacture occurs in the blades, and much of this food is then conducted through the petiole to other parts of the plant. Water and minerals move into the blade through the petiole. Small, leaf-like **stipules** are frequently found at the base of the petiole, along with an axillary bud. The development of an axillary bud results in the production of secondary branches, flowers, or both, depending upon the type of bud.[3] ◄

Using the above passage and the drawing, see if you can fill in the following chart, which breaks down the structure of a leaf.

BASIC STRUCTURE OF THE LEAF

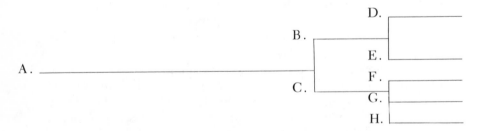

This may not have been the way you would break down the structure of a leaf, but it is one way of remembering the basic parts. Check your answers

---

[3]Muller, *op. cit.*, p. 94.

with these: A. leaf; B. petiole; C. blade; D. stipule; E. axillary bud; F. flat blade; G. needle-like blade; H. scale-like blade. You may argue that the stipule is not a part of the petiole and feel that a third major subdivision of the leaf should be made. That would be correct too. But remember, the reason for examining these patterns of science writing is to help you understand and remember what you read. There is no *one* right way.

Actually, with a diagram such as the one in the sample paragraph, the classification is all done for you. Again, don't ever overlook a reference to a chart or a diagram because they are all aids to reading comprehension.

Descriptive classifications

Another use of the classification pattern is to describe things. Here is an example from a chemistry textbook:

▶   Two primary classifications of the elements are **metals** and **nonmetals.** We are probably more familiar with metals because of their widespread use in tools, materials of construction, automobiles, etc. But nonmetals are equally useful in our everyday life as major components of clothing, food, fuel, glass, plastics, wood, etc.

The metallic elements are solids at room temperature (mercury is an exception). They have a high luster, are good conductors of heat and electricity, can be rolled or hammered into sheets (are malleable), and can be drawn into wires (are ductile). In addition to these properties, most metals have a high melting point and a high density. Metals with which we are ordinarily familiar are aluminum, chromium, copper, gold, iron, lead, magnesium, platinum, silver, and tin. Other less familiar but still important metals are calcium, cobalt, potassium, sodium, uranium, and zinc.

Metals have little tendency to combine with each other to form compounds. But many metals readily combine with nonmetals such as chlorine, oxygen, and sulfur to form metallic chlorides, oxides, and sulfides, respectively. The more active metals are found combined with other elements as ores and minerals. A few of the less active ones—such as copper, gold, and silver—are found in a native or free state as well as in ores.

Nonmetals such as carbon, iodine, phosphorus, and sulfur are solids; bromine is a liquid; and oxygen, nitrogen, chlorine, and neon are gases. Nonmetals do not have the properties of metals; that is, they are generally brittle, nonlustrous, normally exist as either gases or solids, have relatively low melting points and densities, and are not good conductors of heat and electricity.[4] ◀

---

[4]From *Foundations of College Chemistry* by Morris Hein. © 1967 by Dickenson Publishing Company, Inc., Belmont, California. Reprinted by permission of the publisher.

In the space below, classify the things being discussed in the previous passage.

Now see if the classification can help you answer these questions. Do not refer back to the selection. Use only your classification chart.

1. What are the two primary classifications of elements?
   a. _____ and b. _____.
2. Name *at least three* properties of metallic elements.
   a. _____
   b. _____
   c. _____
3. Name at least three properties of nonmetallic elements.
   a. _____
   b. _____
   c. _____
4. Which of the elements have little tendency to combine with each other? _____

Check your answers with these: 1. (a) metal; (b) nonmetal; 2. (any three of the following) solid; high luster; good conductors of heat and electricity; can be rolled, hammered, or drawn into wires; 3. (any three of the following) solid or liquid, brittle, nonlustrous, low melting points and densities, not good conductors of heat and electricity; 4. metals.

Again, how you classified or arranged your order of elements is not as important as doing it so that you can answer questions such as the previous ones. Just for comparison, however, notice the classification procedure at the top of page 67. How similar is it to yours?

For many students, the reading of classification patterns can be very easy when they take the time to break each passage down into its major points and minor subdivisions. Of course, not all reading passages are as short as the ones presented for you here. Sometimes an entire chapter may be basically a classification pattern which uses other patterns within it. It would take too much space to reproduce an entire chapter here, but the following passage from a biology book can serve as an example. Several types of writing patterns are used, but the basic one is classification. See if you can recognize the pattern.

▶   By the beginning of the twentieth century the essential facts about the over-all distribution of land mammals were known. When these facts were arranged and generalized, there emerged a pattern of *land*

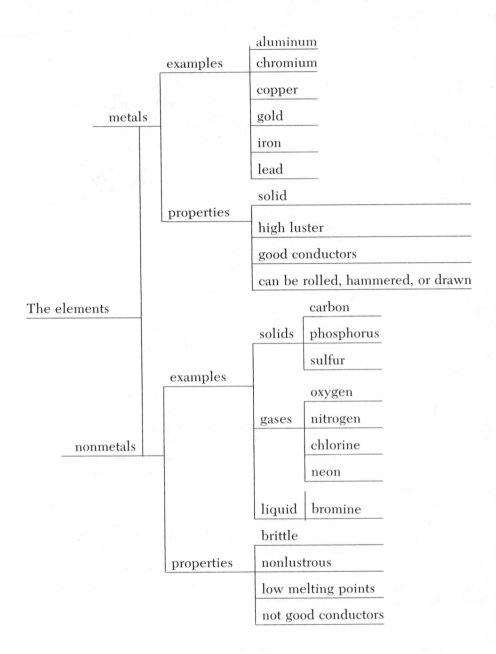

faunal regions. Each region has some measure of general faunal resemblance throughout, and each has distinctions from any other region. The arrangement shown in Figure 5.2 is now usual.

Faunas intergrade everywhere, and there are no such sharp lines in nature as on the map. Note, too, that this particular pattern is pri-

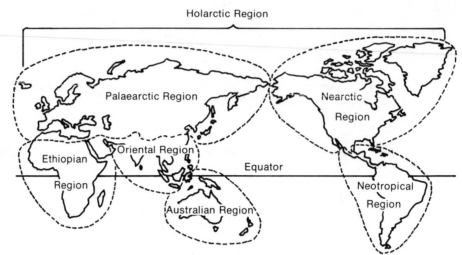

Figure 5.2.   The faunal regions of the world.

marily for mammals and birds;* its application to other groups of
animals and to plants is also generally valid but less clear. Even for
mammals and birds, its application to islands other than those recently connected to continents is misleading. With these provisos
the pattern has a real validity that may be briefly demonstrated.

The *Holarctic† region* has such animals as the timber wolf, hares,
moose (called "elk" in Europe), and stag (called "elk" in America)
that range through most of it and only marginally, if at all, elsewhere.
The New World and Old World parts are distinctive in a lesser way.
For instance, our commonest deer are of a genus (*Odocoileus*) absent
in Eurasia, and the wild boar of Holarctic Eurasia is absent here.
The Holarctic is often separated into *Nearctic* ["new (world) northern"] and the Eurasian *Palaearctic* ["old (world) northern"] subregions.

The *Oriental region* is the haunt of the tiger, Indian elephant (a
different genus from the African elephant), gibbons, and many other
mammals nearly or quite confined to this region. The *Ethiopian region* is especially characterized by the giraffe, zebras, African elephant, and a great abundance of antelopes, some related to Oriental
species and others sharply distinct.

The *Neotropical‡ region* is more distinctive than any of those already mentioned. Among the many mammals nearly or entirely
confined to this region are the guinea pigs and many related rodents,

*The original proposal (by Alfred Russell Wallace) in nearly this form was based on both mammals and
birds.
†"Whole northern."
‡"New (world) tropical." The name is somewhat misleading. An enormous part of this region, in southern
South America, is outside the tropics.

New World monkeys (ceboids), sloths, true anteaters, and armadillos. The *Australian region* is even more distinctive. Its mammalian fauna consists largely of marsupials, and all belong to families that occur nowhere else.§ The peculiar monotremes are also confined to this region. There are some native placental mammals—bats, rats, and a dog—but most of them are also of distinct species or genera.[5] ◄

In the space provided, break the above sample passage down into its major and minor points. Be certain to use the map to which the passage refers.

Without referring back to the reading selection, use only your classification breakdown to answer the following questions.

1. What is being classified?
   _____

2. What are the major divisions?
   a. _____
   b. _____
   c. _____
   d. _____
   e. _____

3. What major division is subdivided?
   _____

4. What are the subdivisions?
   a. _____
   b. _____

5. What common examples are used to describe all of the different regions?
   _____

Compare your answers with these: 1. faunal regions of the world; 2. (a) Holarctic, (b) Oriental, (c) Ethiopian, (d) Neotropical, (e) Australian; 3. Holarctic; 4. (a) Nearctic and (b) Palaearctic; 5. animals of various types.

All of the classification patterns used in this chapter are actually ways of outlining. For instance, this last sample passage could have been outlined like this using both the written passage and the map:

_____

§There are two families of living marsupials in North and South America, one of them including the familiar opossum, but these families are not present in Australia.
[5]Simpson and Beck, *op. cit.*, pp. 727–728.

The Faunal Regions of the World

I. Holarctic Region
   A. Subregions
      1. Nearctic region (new-world northern regions)
      2. Palaearctic region (old-world northern regions)
   B. Animals in areas
      1. timber wolves
      2. hares
      3. moose
      4. stag
II. Oriental Region
   A. Lower Asia
   B. Animals in areas
      1. tiger
      2. Indian elephant
      3. gibbons
III. Ethiopian Region
   A. All except northern Africa
   B. Animals in areas
      1. giraffe
      2. zebras
      3. African elephant
      4. antelope
IV. Neotropical Region
   A. Central and South America
   B. Animals in areas
      1. guinea pigs
      2. rodents
      3. new-world monkeys
      4. sloths
      5. anteaters
      6. armadillos
V. Australian Region
   A. Australia, New Zealand, New Guinea
   B. Animals in areas
      1. marsupials
      2. placental mammals
         a. bats
         b. rats
         c. dogs

What does all this mean to you as a reader of science materials? In reading the classification patterns found in science, your understanding of the content depends on your ability to see the major and minor facts, concepts, or theories being presented. Identification of the classification pattern can help you sort out these characteristics. You can then gear your reading and note-taking procedure to this pattern. (More will be said about note-taking in Chapter 11, but already you should be able to see how the pattern presented here lends itself to good note-taking.) The next time you notice this pattern being used in one of your science class assignments, try using what you were shown here.

SUMMARY

This chapter is the first of six chapters to deal with writing patterns found in science textbooks. The *classification pattern* is defined here as a writing procedure used by scientists to group and subgroup various things, objects, or areas. For example, a writer may wish to discuss the structure of a plant. He may break his topic into various subheadings, such as roots, stems, leaves, or flowers. Even within these subheadings he may break down their parts even further. Recognizing these structural parts in order of importance or position is important to good comprehension and note-taking.

You may now wish to do some or all of the exercises in analyzing the classification pattern on pages 205–208 in the practices section.

6

Analyzing the Process-Description Pattern

The total picture. Chapter 5 introduced you to one commonly used writing pattern found in science, the classification pattern. This chapter continues Step Three: *Analyze for Comprehension* with the process-description pattern. Science is concerned with processes, or how things work. Usually this writing pattern is accompanied by charts and diagrams. Such a pattern requires you to read not only the text, but the diagrams as well. Several examples of this pattern are presented for you here.

Explore this chapter before reading closely.

What is a process?

Science is concerned with structure (How is it organized?) and function or process (What does it do? or How does it work?). For instance, a biologist is concerned not only with what a cell is and its composition, but also with the reason for its existence and why and how it divides into another cell. He looks for the purpose behind the process he is investigating.

A process description provides an order or sequence. It gives you a system, and a system is easier to remember than a collection of separate, seemingly unrelated bits of information.

Process-description pattern without visual aids

Some processes are easy enough to explain in the text of a book without requiring visual aids (charts, pictures, diagrams, tables). Here is a passage dealing with the sequence of heart action. Notice how the heartbeat process is explained.

▶ The sequence of heart action is as follows: The thin-walled auricles fill with blood from the great veins, then contract, moving the blood into the ventricles. As the latter begin to contract, the bicuspid and tricuspid valves are closed by the increasing pressure of the blood. The semilunar valves are still closed, so the blood is blocked in all directions and its pressure rises. When pressure in the ventricles exceeds that in the arteries, the semilunar valves open and blood spurts into the arterial system. Then the cycle is repeated. The only rest for heart muscle throughout life is in the short intervals while the chambers are filling.[1] ◀

Can you break the sequence of heart action into its major divisions or phases? Try it, using the outline below:

I. _____
II. _____
III. _____
    A. _____
    B. _____
IV. _____
    A. _____
    B. _____
V. _____

Compare your outline with the following. There may be some variety in wording, but the basic divisions or phases should be approximately the same.

I. Auricles fill with blood from veins.
II. Auricles contract, moving blood to ventricles.
III. Ventricles contract.
    A. Bicuspid and tricuspid valves close from pressure.
    B. Closed semilunar valves block blood, causing pressure.
IV. Ventricles open.
    A. Excessive pressure forces semilunar valves open.
    B. Blood spurts into arterial system.
V. Cycle repeated.

This is a breakdown of the sequence of heart action as the passage from the text explains it. As a reader, you must "see" how the process works. Taking the time to outline a passage such as this one can be a great aid to comprehending process-description patterns.

Try the following process-description passage[2] which explains a mathematical process for handling large numbers.

---

[1] From *General Zoology* by Tracy I. Storer and Robert L. Usinger. Copyright © 1965 by McGraw-Hill Book Company, Inc. Copyright 1943, 1951, 1957 by McGraw-Hill Book Company, Inc.

[2] From *Physics*, 2nd Edition, by the Physical Science Study Committee. Copyright © 1965 by Education Development Center.

► The span of time since the first animals came to live on dry land includes something like 12,000,000,000,000,000 seconds. The time it takes a light ray to pass through a windowpane is about 1/100,000,000,000 part of a second. Such numbers are impossibly clumsy to learn or to use. But since we must be prepared to use large and small numbers, large and small counts, throughout physics, we must find a way to handle them.

There is an easy, compact way. Any number can be written as the product of a number between one and ten and a number which is a power of ten. For example, we can write 769 as 7.69×100; and 0.0043 is $4.3 \times 1/1000$. The number at the beginning of this section is $1.2 \times 10,000,000,000,000,000$. We shall usually write our numbers this way, but in order to avoid writing zeros till our hands hurt, we shall use an abbreviation. Instead of 100 we write 10^2; in place of $1/1000$, which equals $1/10^3$, we write 10^{-3}, and in place of the long one we write 1.2×10^{16}. The exponent, at the upper right of the 10, tells how many zeros in the power of ten, and we use the minus sign to say that we deal with thousandths instead of with thousands.

A few more examples should make the system clear:

$$3270 = 3.27 \times 10^3.$$
$$0.124 = 1.24 \times 10^{-1}.$$
$$652,000 = 6.52 \times 10^5. \blacktriangleleft$$

This passage is not like the previous one. You can't easily plot the process in an outline form. Yet it is still an example of the process-description pattern because it explains how you can write long numbers in a shorter form.

See whether you understand the process by converting these numbers to shorter forms:
1. 12,000,000,000,000,000 = _____
2. $1/1,000,000$ = _____
3. 6750 = _____
4. 500,000 = _____
5. 0.631 = _____

Compare your answers with the following: (1) 1.2×10^{16}; (2) 10^{-6}; (3) 6.75×10^3; (4) 5×10^5; (5) 6.31×10^{-1}.

If you had trouble answering these questions, reread the passage. This time notice that the process could be divided into major parts: (1) the process of converting *thousands* into exponents; and (2) the process of converting *thousandths* into exponents. Both processes are used to tell how many zeros there are in the power of ten.

As you read your science textbooks and notice that a process is being explained without visual aids, take the time to determine what the process is, and how the process works.

Process-description pattern with visual aids

More often than not, the process-description pattern of writing is accompanied by charts, diagrams, or tables. This requires that you read both the text itself and the visual aid, sometimes jumping back and forth from text passage to diagram.

▶   *Mitosis.* Cells multiply chiefly by **mitosis**, a rather complex process that involves, importantly, an equal division of the nuclear chromatin in kind and amount (Figure 6.1). Cell division by mitosis is common to all animals from amoeba to man and in all plants except bacteria and blue-green algae. Mitosis is active during embryonic development, in growth, in repair of injury, and in replacement of body covering at molting. It is also the process involved in malignant growths (tumors, cancer). As seen in living cells it is a continuous dynamic process, but for convenience in study it is divided into several stages, as follows: (1) prophase, (2) metaphase, (3) anaphase, and (4) telophase. Cells not undergoing mitosis are said to be in the interphase, or are called metabolic cells, because metabolic processes are going on constantly within them.[3] ◀

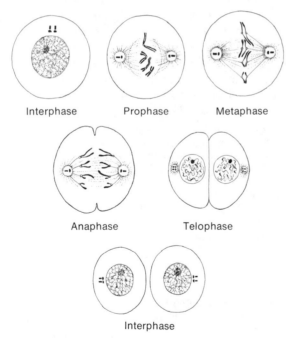

Figure 6.1.   Stages in mitosis.

---

[3]Storer and Usinger, *op. cit.*, p. 46.

Check your comprehension by answering these questions:

1. What process is being discussed? _____

_____

2. How many stages are there in the process? _____

_____

3. List the names of the stages: _____

_____

4. To what does *interphase* refer? _____

_____

5. What function does Figure 6-1 serve? _____

_____

_____

If you were reading this passage from your textbook, you would find each of the stages of the process being discussed and elaborated upon. But even the short passage and visual aid shown here serve as examples of the use of the process-description writing pattern. Check your answers with these: 1. Mitosis (Again a bold heading is a tip-off, but even more, the first sentence of the selection uses the words *complex process.*) 2. Four stages (They have even been numbered for you in the text.) 3. prophase, metaphase, anaphase, and telophase (Notice that each one is a *phase*: *pro* means before, *meta* means change or turn over, *ana* means up or toward, and *telo* means end. Step Two is useful at this point in helping you remember what each phase does.) 4. *Interphase* refers to the state in which cells are not undergoing mitosis. 5. The figure shows the process of mitosis from beginning to end.

By now you should begin to see how the various steps mentioned in this book should be used together. The previous passage is easy to understand if you utilize the headings, captions under diagrams, and vocabular skills. Combined with an analysis of the writing pattern in order to distinguish main ideas from subordinate ideas, the total process can't help but improve your comprehension. But you must use the steps in the process for better reading.

Now as you read your science assignments, explore them before reading carefully, check the vocabulary, and feel at ease when you notice the writing patterns of classification (Chapter 5) or process-description.

SUMMARY

Analyzing the process-description pattern simply means to be aware of two major reading purposes when you encounter the pattern: (1) learn exactly what the process is, and (2) learn exactly how the process works. This can best be done by examining each phase or stage of the process. Putting your vocabulary knowledge to work for you can often help you decipher new words or terms used in discussing the process.

You may now wish to do some or all of the exercises pertaining to this lesson on pages 209–210 in the practices section.

7

Analyzing the Factual-Statement Pattern

The total picture. The factual-statement pattern, the third science-writing pattern presented in this book, is different from the factual types of statements found in the other subject areas. In science, the word *fact* is a very exacting term and is often used in a different sense from the layman's usage. Before a scientist will accept something as a fact, he subjects it to much experimentation and observation. In using this pattern, scientists often form definitions, compare or contrast factual things, or use facts as illustrations or examples. This chapter will present some examples of this pattern after defining it in more detail.

Explore this chapter before reading it closely.

What is a fact?

Suppose someone said to you, "John F. Kennedy was the greatest President we have ever had." Would you consider the statement fact or opinion? If you agreed, you might tend to say the statement is fact, but the only factual part of the statement is that Kennedy was President. The word *greatest* is a value judgment, and it makes the statement an opinion. That distinction between fact and opinion is easy to understand, but it isn't always this easy.

Check your ability to recognize factual statements by circling the number of each of the following statements you consider a fact.

1. December is always a winter month.
2. Unsupported objects will fall to the earth.
3. Science is a boring subject.
4. The moon is 240,000 miles from earth.
5. 5^4 means $5 \times 5 \times 5 \times 5 = 625$.
6. The temperature at which water freezes is called 0° C or 32° F.

Probably you circled numbers 2, 4, 5, and 6. Number 1 is not a fact because December is a summer month in the southern hemisphere. Number 3 is a value judgment, and while science may be a boring subject to many students it isn't to many others; hence this can't be a fact. Now if you want to get very technical, you can probably find some case in which each of the statements is nonfactual. A balloon filled with helium won't fall to the earth. The moon isn't always exactly 240,000 miles from the earth. But in general these are taken as facts.

Scientists attempt to deal with facts as much as possible, since facts are the real basis for science. Facts are not something scientists make up or develop. For instance, objects heavier than air will fall to the ground, not because science says so but because so far every heavier-than-air object held up unsupported falls to the ground. This is generalized into a theory which predicts that all bodies heavier than air will fall to the ground. Each time an object falls to the ground, the theory is confirmed.

Would you consider this paragraph a factual statement?

▶   The heart in a quiet normal person contracts about 72 times per minute and pumps about 60 cc. of blood per "beat." The total volume of blood is about 6,000 cc., and all of it could pass through the heart in 100 beats. During a life of 70 years the heart may contract three billion times and move nearly two hundred million liters of blood. In some small birds and mammals the heart beats 200 to 400 times per minute.[1] ◀

Most of us will probably accept the facts that the heart in a quiet normal person contracts about 72 times per minute and pumps about 60 cc. of blood per "beat" because the statement is based on the observation of the hearts of many quiet normal persons. The "facts" will only change if the heart of normal persons begins to change. The scientist might, however, say the statement is not fact, but a hypothesis, or logical guess, that if every quiet normal person's heart could be checked the above statement might be true.

A *fact*, as used in this chapter, is any statement that defines something or explains its actions and which, so far, has not been disproved. Here is an example:

▶   *Conductive* (or *vascular*) *tissue* is concerned with transport in a plant, as the name implies. There are two kinds of conductive tissue. The *xylem* carries water and dissolved minerals upward from the roots, where they are absorbed from the soil, to all other parts of the plant. Xylem cells, like all other specialized types, begin life as unspecialized cells, derived from a meristem. As they mature, their

[1]Storer and Usinger, *op. cit.*, p. 113.

walls become heavily thickened, often with conspicuous spiral bands. In the more highly evolved plants, adjacent xylem cells, one above the other, eventually lose their end walls and fuse with each other to form a continuously open vessel running up the axis of the plant. They also lose their cytoplasm and nuclei, but though they are dead, their function as conducting vessels is unimpaired. As we shall see, each plant organ is supplied with an abundance of xylem vessels.

The second kind of conductive tissue is *phloem.* It carries the food materials manufactured in the leaves to all parts of the plant, both above and below the leaves. Mature phloem cells are elongate cylinders whose walls are not so heavily thickened as those of xylem cells. Nor do the end walls of the phloem cells break down. Instead, connection between phloem cells is effected through a series of pores in their end walls, which are appropriately called *sieve plates.* The nuclei of phloem cells disintegrate, but their cytoplasmic contents remain, fusing through the sieve-plate pores and forming a protoplasmic highway along which food is carried.[2] ◄

Here now are some statements taken from the passage. Circle the number of the statements you think are facts.
1. Conductive (or vascular) tissue is concerned with transport in a plant, as the name implies.
2. There are two kinds of conductive tissue.
3. The xylem carries water and dissolved minerals upward from the roots.
4. The phloem carries the food materials manufactured in the leaves to all parts of the plant.
5. Mature phloem cells are elongate cylinders whose walls are not so heavily thickened as those of xylem cells.

You probably circled all of them, as you should have. All of these are statements of facts, facts which have been demonstrated or verified by observations of many scientists. The writers of that selection can make a statement such as "Conductive tissue is concerned with transport in a plant," knowing that other scientists will accept it as a fact—at least until scientists prove otherwise. This, then, is what is meant by facts in science.

Analyzing the facts from the observation pattern

Now let's look more closely at the writing pattern itself. Go back to the previous reading selection (the one dealing with conductive tissue) and read it again. Then answer these questions without looking back:

---

[2]Simpson and Beck, *op. cit.*, p. 92.

_____ 1. Which of the following choices best states the main idea of the selection:
   a. Conductive tissue is complex.
   b. Conductive tissue is of two types.
   c. Conductive tissue carries materials throughout a plant.
_____ 2. The function of the xylem cells is to
   a. carry food materials manufactured in the leaves.
   b. carry water and minerals from the roots.
   c. carry water and materials manufactured in the roots.
_____ 3. The function of the phloem cell is to
   a. carry food materials and water manufactured in the roots.
   b. carry water and minerals manufactured in the leaves.
   c. carry food materials manufactured in the leaves.
_____ 4. T or F: When xylem cells die their function is unimpaired.
_____ 5. T or F: The connection of phloem cells is effected through a series of pores in their end walls.

Check your answers with these: 1. c, 2. b, 3. c, 4. T, 5. T. If you answered all five of these questions, you have a good grasp of the difference between the major and minor points in the selection. Skip over to the next boldface heading. If you didn't answer all the questions, read on.

The reading selection on conductive tissue is filled with facts, one after another. That doesn't make it an easy pattern to read and remember. How can a reader tell which of all these facts is the most important? Take another look at the opening lines reproduced for you here:

▶   *Conductive* (or *vascular*) *tissue* is concerned with transport in a plant, as the name implies. There are two kinds of conductive tissue. The *xylem* carries water and dissolved minerals upward from the roots . . . .[3] ◀

First, notice that the opening sentence does two things: it italicizes *conductive tissue* and it states not what conductive tissue is, but the function it serves: transportation. Usually, the first sentence in a paragraph states the main idea. In this case the main idea is that conductive tissue is concerned with transportation in plants. To find out what is meant, read more of the passage.

The second sentence still doesn't tell you what is meant by transport (though you should know that the word has to do with movement or carrying), but it does divide conductive tissue into two kinds. So far you might have something like this pictured in your mind:

---
[3]*Ibid.*, p. 92.

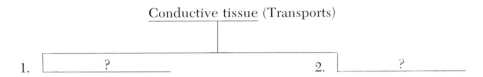

Conductive tissue (Transports)

1. [?]   2. [?]

The third sentence gives you the name of one of the two kinds of conductive tissue, *xylem* (it is italicized for emphasis), and tells you it carries (transports) water and dissolved minerals upward from the roots. Now you have the following:

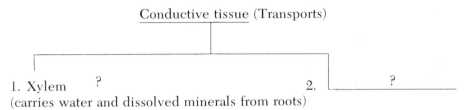

Conductive tissue (Transports)

1. Xylem   ?   2. [?]
(carries water and dissolved minerals from roots)

The main idea (conductive tissue transports in a plant) and one of the details of the main idea (*xylem*, one type of conductive tissue, transports water and dissolved minerals from the roots) have been given to you. The rest of the paragraph gets even more detailed as it explains what the xylem cells look like and how they fuse with each other.

The second paragraph in the selection begins:

► The second kind of conductive tissue is *phloem*. It carries the food materials manufactured in the leaves to all parts of the plant, both above and below the leaves. . . .[4] ◄

Now you have the second kind of conductive tissue, as the second sentence in the first paragraph promised you. Putting it all together, you have the following diagram:

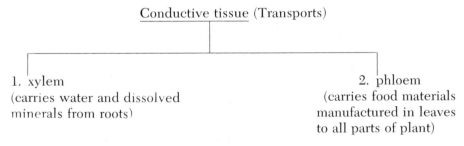

Conductive tissue (Transports)

1. xylem   2. phloem
(carries water and dissolved   (carries food materials
minerals from roots)   manufactured in leaves
                                   to all parts of plant)

If you wanted to utilize all the information in the selection comprising the description of both kinds of tissue, you might end with this:

---

[4]*Ibid.*, p. 92.

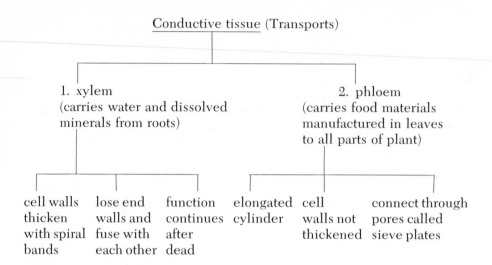

Conductive tissue (Transports)

1. xylem
(carries water and dissolved
minerals from roots)

2. phloem
(carries food materials
manufactured in leaves
to all parts of plant)

| cell walls thicken with spiral bands | lose end walls and fuse with each other | function continues after dead | elongated cylinder | cell walls not thickened | connect through pores called sieve plates |

Whether or not you actually plot out the reading selection on paper is up to you. But at least in your mind you should be able to recognize the main points or facts and the minor facts used as supporting detail. How thorough you are in examining the details depends on how thoroughly you want to read. The diagrams are used here mostly as a means to show you which facts being presented are more important than others. The use of diagrams is recommended, however, as a note-taking device, at least until such time as you no longer feel the need for them.

Defining with facts

Scientists often use facts as definitions or as examples to help clarify definitions. Notice in the following passage how the writer defines the term and then uses facts as examples.

▶   We use the term **solubility** to describe the amount of one substance that will dissolve into another. For example, 36.0 grams of sodium chloride, NaCl, will dissolve in 100 grams of water at 20°C. We say, then, that the solubility of NaCl in water is 36.0 grams per 100 grams of water at this temperature.
    Solubility is often used in a relative way. We say a substance is very soluble, moderately soluble, slightly soluble, or insoluble. Although these terms are not very accurate in indicating how much solute will dissolve, they are frequently used to describe the solubility of a substance.
    Two other terms often used to describe solubility are "miscible" and "immiscible." Substances that are capable of mixing and forming a solution are **miscible;** those that do not form solutions or are generally insoluble in each other are **immiscible.** Methyl alcohol and

water are miscible in each other in all proportions. Oil and water are immiscible, forming two separate layers when they are mixed.[5] ◄

Check to see whether you understand what is meant by defining with facts by answering these questions.

1. What major term is being defined? _____
_____

2. Define it. _____
_____

3. What observed facts are used as examples of the term? _____
_____

4. What minor terms associated with the major term are being defined?
_____
_____

5. Define them. _____
_____

6. What observed facts are used as examples? _____
_____
_____

Check your answers with these:
1. Solubility
2. The amount of one substance that will dissolve into another.
3. 36.0 grams of sodium chloride, NaCl, will dissolve in 100 grams of water at 20°C.
4. Miscible and immiscible.
5. *Miscible* is the term that refers to substances capable of mixing and forming a solution; *immiscible* refers to a substance unable to form solutions.
6. Miscible substances are methyl alcohol and water; immiscible substances are oil and water.

If you had no trouble with the questions, move on to the next boldface heading. If you are still a bit hazy about this writing pattern, perhaps the outline at the top of page 84 will make it clearer.

Here are all the "facts" based on observation being used:

1. Solubility is a condition which exists in life.
2. 36.0 grams of sodium chloride (NaCl) will dissolve in 100 grams of water at 20°C.
3. There are degrees of solubility: very soluble, moderately soluble, slightly soluble, or insoluble.

---

[5]Hein, *op. cit.,* p. 189.

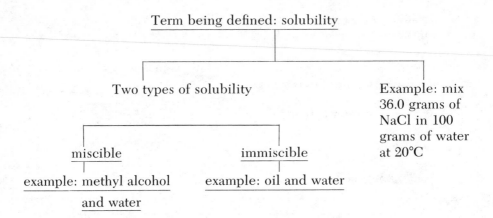

4. There are two other terms often used for soluble and insoluble: miscible and immiscible.
5. Methyl alcohol and water are miscible.
6. Oil and water are immiscible.

Because there are so many facts being used to define the term solubility, the writing pattern becomes one of defining with facts.

Comparisons using facts

Another way that science writers use facts is to compare or contrast two or more things. Usually the comparison is done for a specific purpose, such as defining terms or theories. But the difference between the comparison-using-facts pattern and the definition-using-facts pattern is that the definitions are secondary in importance to stressing the comparison. As you read the following passage, note that two terms are being defined but the major point being made is the difference between the two terms.

► Substances whose aqueous solutions are conductors of electricity are called **electrolytes.** Substances whose solutions are nonconductors are known as **nonelectrolytes.** In general, the classes of compounds which are electrolytes are acids, bases, and salts. Solutions of certain oxides are also conductors because they form an acid or a base when dissolved in water. One major difference between electrolytes and nonelectrolytes is that electrolytes exist as ions or are capable of producing ions in solution, whereas nonelectrolytes do not have this property. Solutions that contain a sufficient number of ions will conduct an electric current. Many city water supplies contain enough dissolved ionic matter to cause the light to glow dimly when tested in the conductivity apparatus. Table 7.1 lists some common electrolytes and nonelectrolytes.[6] ◀

Electrolytes	*Nonelectrolytes*
H_2SO_4	$C_{12}H_{22}O_{11}$ (Sugar)
HCl	C_2H_5OH (Ethyl alcohol)
HNO_3	$C_3H_5(OH)_3$ (Glycerol)
NaOH	CH_3OH (Methyl alcohol)
$HC_2H_3O_2$	$CO(NH_2)_2$ (Urea)
NH_4OH	O_2 (Oxygen)
K_2SO_4	
$NaNO_3$	

Table 7.1. Representative electrolytes and nonelectrolytes

Check your understanding of the passage by answering these questions.

1. What is being contrasted? _____

2. What is being defined? _____

3. Define both terms: _____

4. What does *aqueous* mean? _____
5. What is the major difference between the two terms?

Compare your answers with the following:

1. The difference between electrolytes and nonelectrolytes.
2. Electrolytes and nonelectrolytes.
3. *Electrolytes* are substances whose aqueous solutions conduct electricity; *nonelectrolytes* do not have the conducting property.
4. Water, or like water.
5. The major difference between the two terms is that electrolytes exist as ions and are capable of producing ions in water; nonelectrolytes can't.

As before, if you were able to answer these questions and understand the use of facts for comparison purposes, skip to the next boldface heading. If you still don't quite understand, read on.

Go back and reread the first two sentences of the reading selection. Notice that each sentence is defining a term. The terms have to do with a

_____
[6]*Ibid.*, p. 215.

substance's ability or lack of ability to conduct electricity when in liquid form. The third and fourth sentences give you some classes of electrolytes which do conduct electricity. Then you get an important phrase in the fifth sentence: "One major difference between. . . ." The words *major* and *difference* are important and should alert you to pay attention. It is in this sentence and the next two that the business about ions is explained. The last sentence refers you to Table 7.1, which has a list of examples of both electrolytes and nonelectrolytes. Almost every statement in the paragraph and the table can be considered fact. There is no hypothesis or guesswork, no process, no breakdown of parts. There is simply one fact after another, facts which have been proved by observation and can easily be proved by you if you wish to check each solution experimentally.

There are, naturally, many other ways to use facts in writing. Nevertheless, an awareness of some of these factual-statement patterns can make your reading easier if you can distinguish how the author is using his facts, which are the most important, and which are used for supporting detail.

One more time: What is a fact?

Many arguments are constantly created over such things as "Columbus discovered America," or "The Civil War was fought because of the slavery issue," or "Lincoln emancipated the Negroes," or "When a tree falls in a wood with no one around there is no sound." Today's facts are sometimes tomorrow's fiction. Science continues to pursue facts about the phenomenon known as life. Just remember that what you read as "fact" in your science textbook could possibly be proved wrong in the future. Not too long ago, it was a "fact" that the atom couldn't be smashed.

SUMMARY

This chapter deals with the factual-statement pattern of writing found in science textbooks. The purpose of the chapter is to provide sample passages which use facts in various ways. While facts can be used in as many writing patterns as there are writers, some of the more frequent uses seem to be in presenting facts to define things, to compare or contrast things, and as examples or illustrations.

In science the word *fact* has a more exacting meaning than in other areas. *"Factual statement,"* as used in this chapter, refers to a statement which, because of scientific observation and experimentation, defines something, or explains its actions, and which, so far, has not been disproved.

8

Analyzing the Problem-Solving Pattern

The total picture. The problem-solving pattern is the fourth type of science-writing pattern to be presented in this book. This chapter is concerned with the passages in science textbooks which describe or recount questions in science that have been answered through experimentation. In a way you might consider the problem-solving pattern as a history of scientific experimentation. Bear in mind, however, that problem-solving is not the purpose of science. It is simply a technique for obtaining information.

Remember that all of the writing patterns in this section are still part of Step Three: *Analyze for Comprehension.* As you learn about each of these patterns, utilize what you have learned about the other steps.

Explore this chapter before reading closely.

The problem-solving pattern

The problem-solving pattern is not a difficult one to recognize or read. Basically, you should read this pattern with three questions in mind: (1) what is the basic question; (2) what kind of observation was made to answer the question; and (3) how do we know that the question was answered?

Read the following problem-solving pattern, keeping the three questions in mind.

►   Nor is a concern with theory distracting or wasteful, for when, armed with an advance in theory, men turn to application of a science, how rapidly matters march. And although applied science may advance in a purely empirical fashion without theory, how slow and fumbling that is in comparison.

    As an example, consider the history of infectious disease. Until nearly the dawn of the nineteenth century, doctors had been, by and large, helpless in the face of the vast plagues and epidemics that periodically swept across the land. And of the diseases that plagued mankind, one of the worst was smallpox. Not only did it spread like wildfire; not only did it kill one in three; but even those who survived were unfortunate, for their faces might easily be left so pitted and scarred that one could scarcely endure the sight of them.

One attack of smallpox, however, insured immunity to future attacks. For that reason, a very mild case of smallpox, leaving one virtually unscarred, was far, far better than none at all. In the former case, one was forever safe; in the latter, forever under the threat. In such places as Turkey and China, there were attempts, consequently, to catch the disease from those with mild cases. There was even deliberate inoculation with matter from the blisters produced by mild smallpox. The risk was terrible, for sometimes the disease, when caught, proved not mild at all in the new host.

In the early eighteenth century, such inoculation was introduced into England but did not really prove popular. However, the subject was in the air and under discussion and an English physician, Edward Jenner (1749-1823), began to consider the matter. There was an old-wives' tale in his native country of Gloucestershire to the effect that anyone who caught cowpox (a mild disease common to cattle that resembled smallpox in some ways) was thereafter immune not only to cowpox but to smallpox as well.

Jenner, after long and careful observation, decided to test this. On May 14, 1796, he found a milkmaid who had cowpox. He took the fluid from a blister on her hand and injected it into a boy who, of course, got cowpox in his turn. Two months later, he inoculated the boy again, not with cowpox, but with smallpox. It did not touch the youngster. In 1798, after repetition of the experiment, he published his findings. He coined the word "vaccination" to describe the technique. This is from the Latin word, *"vaccinia,"* for cowpox, which, in turn, comes from the Latin word, *"vacca,"* for cow.

Such was the dread of smallpox that for once an advance was greeted and accepted with almost no suspicion. Vaccination spread like wildfire over Europe and the disease was vanquished. Smallpox has never since been a major problem in any of the medically advanced nations. It was the first serious disease in the history of mankind to be so rapidly and completely brought under control.[1] ◄

To check your comprehension of the passage, answer these questions:
1. What was the question (problem)? _____

_____

_____

[1]From *A Short History of Biology* by Isaac Asimov. Copyright © 1964 by Isaac Asimov. Reprinted by permission of Doubleday & Company, Inc.

2. What observations were made to obtain the answer? _____

_____

_____

_____

3. How do we know that the question was answered? _____

_____

Compare your answers with the following. Your wording will no doubt be different but the basic points mentioned in the answers given here should also be included in your answers.

1. The question was whether inoculating someone with cowpox would make that person immune to smallpox, a much more serious disease.

2. A boy was inoculated with fluid from a milkmaid's cowpox blister. This resulted in the boy's catching cowpox. Two months later the boy was inoculated with smallpox and failed to catch it.

3. The experiment was repeated successfully.

There are many other details in the description of Jenner's experiments but they are not as important as the three basic questions you just answered. Usually minor points are easier to remember once you've located the main ones. For instance, the dates of Jenner's experiments were not basic points to remember.

The main point of that problem-solving passage was to show you how vaccination against smallpox was developed. A good idea, then, is to use the three guide questions presented earlier in analyzing the problem-solving pattern. The ability to isolate these main ideas from supporting details will improve your comprehension and make later recall easier.

Variety in the problem-solving pattern

Two different passages are going to be presented for you, both dealing with the same experiment. Both are taken from science books. After each selection answer the three guide questions.

Selection A:

▶   One of Rutherford's greatest discoveries is an excellent example of this: among his research students at Manchester was a German, Geiger, whose name is perpetuated in the Geiger counter, one of the most important tools in atomic work today. To him he suggested [Rutherford suggested to Geiger] following up something which had, some years before, struck him as curious—that a beam of alpha particles from a radioactive source was scattered in passing through a thin film of aluminum. (The effect on the invisible rays was like that on a beam from a Kleig light when, in order not to be unkind to the fading beauties of a film star, it is masked with butter muslin.) Geiger and a colleague, Marsden, set to work. They used thin films of gold

which is almost "transparent" to alpha rays, but they found that a considerable proportion of the rays were deflected to an angle of ninety
degrees. Rutherford was flabbergasted. "It's as though a fifteen-inch
shell were being bounced off a sheet of tissue paper," he said.

Alpha rays were not easily deflected in this way. In experiments
an enormous electric field was needed to turn them through an angle
of ninety degrees. How could such an electric field exist in such a
thin piece of foil? It was baffling, and for days Rutherford went
around the laboratory humming dolefully "Fight the good Fight"
—a sure sign that he was unhappily perplexed. Then one day he
bounced into the laboratory humming "Onward Christian Sol-
diers"—a sure sign that he was in great good humor. "Geiger," he
cried, "I now know why your particles are kicked around and what
an atom looks like!"

This was how he had reasoned on the facts available: the particles fired by an exploding radioactive atom traveled in straight lines
(like the buckshot from the gun). These alpha particles passed
through matter, not by pushing the atoms aside nor by swerving to
avoid them, but by *passing through* the atoms themselves. Therefore, atoms could not be solid as the prevailing idea then was. "So,"
argued Rutherford, "they must be like solar systems—not solid
spheres." The invading alpha particles would thus be able to tra-
verse the empty space between the central sun and the planets of this
system. This system would be held together by the fact that the
"planets" would be negatively charged electrons and the "sun" a
positively charged nucleus. This nucleus would contain most of the
mass of the atom, but would be a relatively small part of its volume
as contained by the circumference of the electrons in their orbits.
The strong central field which would thus be created would account
for the bending of the alpha rays, since the positively charged alpha
particles (helium nuclei, in fact) would be violently repelled if they
came near the positively charged nucleus.

He put forward his hypothesis in 1911, but kept Geiger and Marsden experimentally checking and rechecking for another two years
until their repeated results promoted his hypothesis to a theory, to
be expressed in the Rutherford-Bohr Model (subsequently modified
but the first conceptual "picture"). Bohr, who had come to Rutherford as a twenty-seven-year-old mathematician (redeemed by a pair
of football boots) worked out the orbits of the electrons on a basis
which has stood the test of time and the test of millions of experiments. In its simplest form—the hydrogen atom—a single electron
rotates around a single proton. The outer boundary which it patrols
gives the atom a diameter which is about one hundred millionth of
an inch. The nucleus—the single proton—has a diameter of only a
tenth of a million-millionth of an inch. In the heavier atoms the or-

bits get more complicated until the model of the uranium atom, with its ninety-two electrons, looks like a ball of knitting wool.

So *inductive* science — experiment to theory, with theory confirmed by experiment — has taken us a long way from the solid atoms of Democritus, *deductively* conceived in the fifth century B.C.[2] ◄

Check your understanding of the passage by answering these questions:

1. What was the question (problem)? _____

_____

_____

_____

2. What observations were made to obtain the answer? _____

_____

_____

_____

3. How do we know that the question was answered? _____

_____

Before checking your answers, read the following passage.

Selection B:

►   Shortly after their [Rutherford and Geiger] discovery, it was recognized that the α-particles emitted during radioactive decay could be used as a sensitive probe in experiments dealing with the nature of matter. By 1910, such experiments were under way in Rutherford's laboratory. Rutherford and Geiger used the apparatus shown in Figure 8.1 for the study of the deflections of directed α-rays by sheets of gold foil about 1000 atoms thick. The entire apparatus was enclosed in an evacuated chamber to prevent extraneous deflections by air molecules. A cylindrical fluorescent screen was placed around the gold foil, and a hole was cut in the screen to permit the α-ray beam to impinge directly on the gold foil. The course of the α-particle could be deduced from the position of the flash of light whenever an α-particle collided with the screen. By such studies it was established that the bulk of the beam passed through the gold foil without deflection. Very few α-particles were deflected at all, and even when this occurred the deflection was slight.

At the time when Geiger was performing these experiments with the gold foil, a young scientist, named Marsden, arrived at Ruther-

[2]From *Science in Our Lives* by Ritchie-Calder (New York: The New American Library, Signet Key Books, 1954), pp. 34–35.

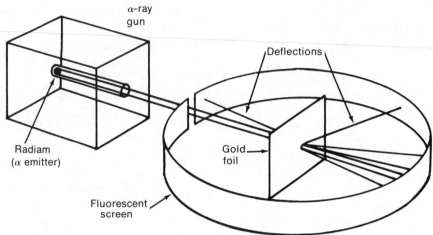

Figure 8.1. Rutherford's apparatus (schematic).

ford's laboratory to study the experimental techniques. Rutherford and Geiger suggested that Marsden carry out a series of experiments in order to see if any of the α-particles bounced back from the gold foil. (Since then, Rutherford, himself, remarked that he considered this as unlikely as a 15-inch shell bouncing back from a sheet of tissue paper.) When Marsden performed these experiments, he found that a few of the α-particles actually did bounce back in the direction from which they came. The number that did were directly proportional to the thickness of the gold foil, and he was able to estimate that, if the gold foil were one atom thick, about one out of 10^8 α-particles directed at the foil would bounce back. These observations formed the first good experimental evidence for the atom as we know it today.

A complete interpretation of these results requires an elaborate mathematical treatment, but an elementary interpretation will reveal the qualitative consequences of this experiment. Let us assume for simplicity that the atoms are little cubes, and that a sheet of foil one atom thick could be made by arranging these atoms in a plane. In Figure 8.2(a) we show a stream of α-particles passing through such a cubical atom. The part of the atom that they hit must be determined by chance, so that we can say that, if only one α-particle out of 10^8 is deflected, this must mean that most of the atom is effectively empty space; most of its mass must be concentrated in a very small fraction of the total space occupied by the atom. To obtain an estimate of the size of this region of concentrated mass, this *nucleus*, let us consider the front view of the atom, shown in Figure 8.2(b). If an atom is such that half of the area presented is effectively empty space and half is massive and impenetrable, then half of the α-particles that strike this atom strike empty space and go through unimpeded, whereas the other half hit the heavy nucleus and bounce back. If we make the nucleus of this hypothetical atom still smaller, as in Figure 8.2(c), where the ratio of the cross-sectional areas is 1 to 10, only 1 out of 10 of the incident α-particles will bounce back. In general, we can say

$$\frac{\text{Number deflected}}{\text{Number striking}} = \frac{A_n}{A_a}$$

where A_n represents the area presented by the nucleus and A_a represents the area presented by the whole atom. On this basis, the observations of Rutherford, Geiger, and Marsden suggest that the area presented by the atom is 10^{+8} times larger than the area presented by the nucleus. The diameter of atoms is roughly 10^{-8} cm; hence the

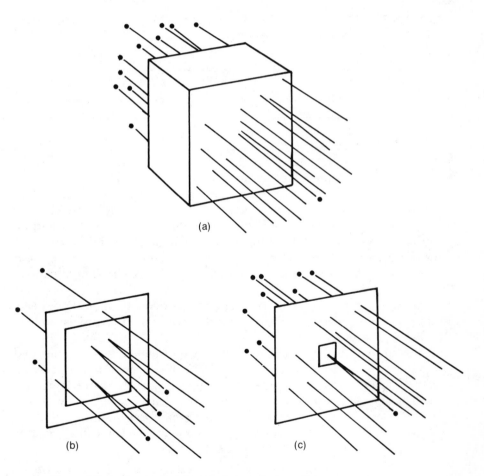

Figure 8.2. α-Ray bombardment of atoms (schematic).

area presented by an atom is $(10^{-8})^2$ cm²; consequently, the effective area of the nucleus is 10^{-24} cm² and the diameter of this nucleus is roughly 10^{-12} cm.

From these experimental observations and conclusions, it is only a step to a planetary model for atoms. It was known at this time that, compared to the proton, the electron has a small mass. Rutherford showed that the results of his experiments were consistent with the planetary model in which the heavy nucleus, only 10^{-12} cm across, takes the role of a miniature sun with the planetary electrons moving in orbits about 10^{-8} cm across. The size of these orbits determines the size of the over-all atom, even though 99.9% of the mass is concentrated in $1/1,000,000,000,000$ (10^{-12}) of the over-all atomic volume. By way of comparison, the atom has a larger fraction of "empty" space than our galaxy.[3] ◄

Check your understanding of this passage by answering these questions:
    1. What was the question (problem)? _____
_____
_____
_____

    2. What observations were made to obtain the answer? _____
_____
_____
_____

    3. How do we know that the question was answered? _____
_____

How similar were your answers to Selections A and B? Despite some minor discrepancies and major differences in reporting the Rutherford experiments with the nature of the atom, the answers should be basically the same. Compare your answers with these. Again, the wording of your answers may vary from the following examples but yours should contain the primary points.

    1. The question was "Why do alpha (α) particles from an x-ray beam bounce back and scatter when passing through certain materials such as aluminum and gold sheets.

    2. In this case the question arose from experimental observations and led to a theory: that atoms are not solid but planetary in structure, with negatively charged electrons orbiting around a positively charged nucleus.

    3. The theory led to a model of the atom that is consistent with the results of a very large number of experiments performed since.

As you can see, the three guide questions can help you extract what is

---

[3]From *Fundamental Chemistry*, 2nd ed., by Donald H. Andrews and Richard J. Kokes. Copyright© 1962, 1965 by John W. Wiley & Sons, Inc.

important from the problem-solving pattern. The basic differences in the two accounts lie in the fact that the authors' purposes for presenting them were different.

"Off-beat" problem-solving patterns

In Chapter 7 it was stated that there are as many writing patterns as there are writers so don't become so absorbed in trying to classify the writing pattern that you miss the ideas being presented. Certain patterns found in science textbooks appear frequently enough to be useful in showing you how to analyze for better comprehension. But not every passage in a science text is a clearcut example.

To illustrate how different writers come up with different patterns, here is an "off-beat" problem-solving pattern. Finding the answers to the three guide questions may not be as easy.

► ### Oersted's Experiment

While magnetic phenomena have been known for thousands of years, a knowledge of their connection with electric currents is only about 150 years old. The word "magnetism" comes from Magnesia, the name of a region in ancient Asia Minor where naturally magnetic pieces of the iron oxide $FeO \cdot Fe_2O_3$, called *lodestones*, are found. The ancients knew that lodestones attract iron objects and can even magnetize such objects so that they, in turn, attract other pieces of iron. It is an easy matter to show that static electric charges and stationary magnets have no attraction for one another, and, as a perhaps unreliable legend relates, it was in the course of a lecture demonstration that electric currents and magnets also do not interact that Hans Oersted (1777–1851) discovered the contrary to be true.

Oersted used an experimental arrangement like that shown in Figure 8.4 at the top of page 96. When a wire is placed parallel to the compass needle and the current turned on, the needle rotates until it is almost perpendicular to the wire. When the wire is initially perpendicular to the compass needle, there is no deflection when the current is turned on. The two conclusions that can be drawn are:

    (1) an electric current somehow exerts a twisting force on a magnet near it;

    (2) the magnitude of the force depends upon the relative orientation of the current and the magnet.[4] ◄

Can you answer these questions?

---

[4]From *Modern Technical Physics* by Arthur Beiser. Copyright © 1966 Addison-Wesley Publishing Company, Ind., Reading, Massachusetts.

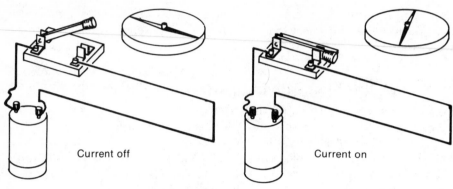

Current off   Current on

Figure 8.4.   Oersted's experiment.

1. What was the question (problem)? _____

_____

_____

_____

2. What observations were made to obtain the answer? _____

_____

_____

_____

_____

3. How do we know that the question was answered? _____

_____

The first question may have given you some second thoughts because as the pattern appears there is no clearcut statement of the problem. In fact, there was no problem that needed solving. You are told that during a lecture an experiment conducted to demonstrate that electric currents and magnets do not interact actually proved the opposite. In a way, the problem was created *after* the experiment. Thus the question became "Why do electric currents and magnets interact?" This led to the belief that the origin of magnetic fields is in the motion of electric charges.

The second question is not difficult. You were told how the experimenter placed a wire and compass needle parallel and turned on the current through the wire, causing the compass needle to turn perpendicular to the wire. When the wire is already perpendicular to the needle, no change occurs. You were also given a diagram to show the equipment and arrangement for the experiment. The problem wasn't really solved, but two conclusions were drawn from the experiment.

The third question is not answered in the selection, but you could repeat the experiment to verify the results.

The following is another example of an "off-beat" problem-solving pattern:

▶ Subjects were "wired" for EEG recording; the experimenter was in another room with the electroencephalograph. As each subject slept, the experimenter watched carefully for the eye movements that indicate dreaming. As soon as such movements were detected, the experimenter would ring a bell in the subject's room, ask him if he had been dreaming, and talk to him for a few minutes by means of an intercom to be sure he was fully awake. The subject would then be allowed to go back to sleep, but would again be awakened as soon as he began to dream.

The usual four or five dream attempts per night rose to ten attempts on the first night dreaming was interrupted and to as many as thirty on the fifth night. Daytime behavior also changed considerably, with increases in irritability, anxiety and tension, difficulty in concentrating, and memory lapses. A majority of participants who were awakened more than three consecutive nights reported a marked increase in appetite and gained an average of a pound a day.

After five nights of dream interruption, the subjects were allowed to sleep through the night. On the first night of normal sleep, subjects who usually dreamed 80 minutes dreamed as long as 150 minutes.

To be sure that the observed changes in behavior were not due merely to loss of sleep, the experimenter repeated the experiment with the same subjects, awakening them the same number of times, but only during nondreaming periods. Under these conditions, none of the signs of upset were present, apparently indicating that the emotional imbalance had been the result of the shortage of dreaming (Dement, 1960).[5] ◀

Apply the same three questions you have been using to the above passage:

1. What was the question (problem)? _____

   _____

   _____

   _____

2. What observations were made to obtain the answer? _____

   _____

   _____

   _____

3. How do we know that the question was answered? _____

   _____

As in the previous example, there is no clear statement of a question or problem. You can infer, however, that the question would be something like "Are dreams necessary?" or "What happens when people are prevented from dreaming?"

The answer to the second question is given in the first paragraph of the passage: for five nights the subject was awakened whenever he began to dream, and his waking behavior was observed, as well as changes in the number of dreaming attempts.

As for the third question, we know only that loss of sleep was eliminated as a possible cause of the behavior changes by repeating the experiment, awakening the subject the same number of times but only during nondreaming periods.

As a reader, you cannot always expect a problem-solving pattern to conform to the three guide questions, but they are still valid questions. You can modify them to help you read for the major ideas of textbook passages dealing with this type of writing pattern.

SUMMARY

The problem-solving pattern is found in passages from science texts which describe or recount past problems in science or discoveries in science made through experimentation. This pattern may be primarily a historical account, a technical account, or a combination of both. Regardless of the fact that writers may not follow the problem-solving pattern in any definite way, there are three good questions to use to help analyze problem-solving passages:

1. What is the question or problem?
2. How was the question answered?
3. How do we know it was answered?

An application of these three questions can help you to separate the major and minor points.

You may now wish to do the exercises on pages 213–214 in the practices section.

9

Analyzing the Experiment-Instructions Pattern

The total picture. Another frequent writing pattern found in science books is the one in which instructions for conducting an experiment are given. This pattern consists of directions—sometimes simple, sometimes complex—that you must carry out carefully. Experiment instructions usually demand that you not only read the directions carefully, but observe reactions, obtain results, and explain what happens. The problem-solving pattern discussed in Chapter 8 deals with how people answered questions through experimentation whereas this pattern requires you to do the experimenting.

If you are not having difficulty following experiment instructions, you may wish to skip over parts of this chapter. Explore it first, however.

Simple experiment instructions

Almost all science courses require that you do some experimental work, usually as a way of demonstrating the ideas presented. Sometimes the experiments are done at home or in the classroom. Other experiments are quite elaborate and require weeks of work in a laboratory. Whether simple or complex, experiment instructions require that you understand what the problem is, that you assume certain things will occur (hypothesize), that you gather facts from the experiment being conducted, and that you record the results and interpret the data.

Here is an example of instructions for a simple experiment. In Chapter 8 you read about the discovery by Oersted that magnetic fields can be produced by electric currents. The following instruction calls for you to conduct the same experiment.

►   Magnetite and magnetized iron are not the only sources of magnetic fields. Let us perform an experiment in which we produce a magnetic field without using such materials.

We attach a long piece of wire to the terminals of a battery through a switch as shown in Figure 9.1. With the switch open, we hold the wire above a compass needle and parallel to it. Then we close the switch. If the current in the wire is sufficiently strong, we see the compass needle suddenly deflected. It now points across the wire. We therefore conclude that electric currents produce magnetic fields in the surrounding space.[1] ◄

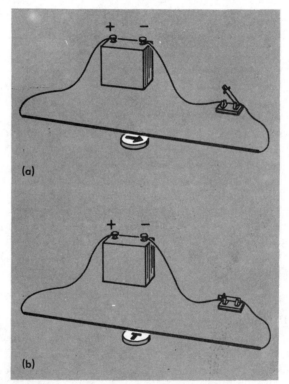

Figure 9.1.   (a) A wire placed over a compass needle and parallel to it. The switch is open, and no current flows in the wire. (b) When current flows, the needle is deflected and points across the wire.

See how well you understand the experiment instructions.

[1] Physical Science Study Committee, *op. cit.*, p. 547.

1. The purpose of the experiment is _____
   _____
   _____
   _____

2. The equipment needed is _____
   _____
   _____

3. The basic steps for performing the experiment are, in order, _____
   _____
   _____
   _____
   _____
   _____

4. The result is _____
   _____
   _____

It's doubtful that you had any real trouble with these questions. For one thing, the experiment had already been described, in Chapter 8, so the details were not new to you. For another, the basic steps are simple. And finally, you were provided with a diagram to help make the reading of the text easier. Compare your answers, which will vary in wording, to the following:

1. The purpose of the experiment is to see if magnetic fields can be produced by sources other than magnetic and magnetized iron (see first paragraph).

2. The equipment needed is a battery, a long wire, a switch, and a compass needle.

3. The basic steps in performing the experiment are these: (1) Attach a long wire to the terminals of a battery and through the switch; (2) With the switch open, hold the wire parallel to and over a compass needle; (3) Close the switch; (4) Observe what happens.

4. The result is that electric current can create a magnetic field.

Another type of experiment instruction is the type given to you as work problems at the end of a chapter or unit. Read the instructions below, looking for the purpose of the experiment, the equipment needed, the steps involved, and the expected conclusion.

▶   A loop of wire *JKL* lies between the pole pieces of a magnet with the plane of the loop parallel to the pole pieces, as shown in Figure 9.2(a). It is connected to a sensitive ammeter whose pointer stands at the center of the scale when there is no current, and which is so constructed that the pointer swings toward the terminal (*P* or *Q*) at which the current enters the ammeter.

(a) Which way does the pointer swing when the loop is pulled out of the field of the magnet? When it is put back as it is in Figure 9.2(a)?

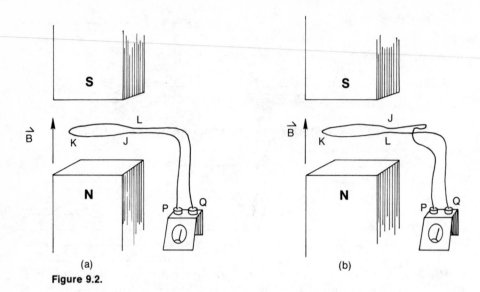

(a)   (b)

Figure 9.2.

(b) Which way does the pointer swing when the loop is put back as it is in Figure 9.2(b)?

(c) How does the pointer move when the loop is turned over from the first position to the second without being taken out of the field of the magnet?[2] ◄

Without actually conducting the experiment, how many of the following questions can you answer?

1. The purpose of the experiment is _____

_____

_____

_____

2. The equipment needed is _____

_____

_____

3. The basic steps for performing the experiment are, in order, _____

_____

_____

_____

_____

_____

4. The result is _____

_____

_____

Compare your responses with the following sample answers. Your wording may vary.

[2]*Ibid.*, p. 592.

1. The purpose of the experiment is to determine whether a magnetically induced current has a clockwise or a counterclockwise direction around the axis of the inducing magnetic field.

2. The equipment needed is a magnet, a loop of wire, and a special type of ammeter.

3. The basic steps would be to set up the equipment as shown in the illustration and then do steps a, b, and c.

4. The result can't be interpreted unless you have previous knowledge about the experiments or about magnetic fields.

The example you just read is more of a problem than an experiment. If you had read the chapter from which this problem was taken, you could probably deduce the answers to a, b, and c from the knowledge gained by reading. However, the problem is presented in such a way that you could actually perform the experiment yourself if you couldn't answer the problem.

Complex experiment instructions

Most of the more complex experiments are conducted in the lab. In Step One you were shown how to explore lab reading assignments by determining what equipment you will need and what you are expected to do with it. Step Three is concerned with how well you can follow the instructions so that you can not only perform the experiment correctly but draw conclusions about it as well.

Turn back to page 23 in Chapter 2. There you will find a laboratory experiment that you have already explored as an exercise. This time read it as carefully as if you were actually going to conduct the experiment. Use these four reading-guide questions:

1. What is the purpose of the experiment?
2. What equipment is needed?
3. What are the basic steps in order of performance?
4. What is the result?

Once you have found the answers to these guide questions, return to this page and write them in the spaces below.

1. The purpose of the experiment is _____

_____

_____

2. The equipment needed is _____

_____

3. The basic steps for performing the experiment are, in order, _____

_____

_____

_____

_____
_____

4. The result is _____
_____
_____

Compare your responses with the following sample answers. Your wording may vary.

    1. The purpose of the experiment is to compare your blood cells with
those of a frog to determine shape, size, and presence or absence of a nucleus.

    2. The equipment needed is a microscope and slides, a cork, a scalpel
blade, cotton, alcohol (70%), acetic acid, frog's blood, and your own blood.

    3. There are two basic steps. The first major step is to examine the
frog's blood by placing a drop on a slide and covering it. Note the size and
shape of red cells and presence of a nucleus. Then add a drop of acetic
acid to kill the red blood cells and make the white blood cells easier to
find. The second major step is to follow the Figure 2.2 directions to obtain
some of your blood. Then examine it as you did the frog's blood.

    4. The result can't be interpreted from the reading alone. You would
have to conduct the experiment to obtain a result unless you already knew
the answers to the questions asked.

    If you had trouble with any of these answers, return to Chapter 2 and
look at the experiment again.

    There is still one other common type of experiment-instruction pat-
tern. This type occurs when you are supposed to read your lab manual
and perform experiments that have already been set up for you. This pattern requires that you not only read, but become acquainted with the apparatus set up for the experiment. The four guide questions presented in
this chapter can still help you read this type of instruction. The difference
is that you must jump back and forth from reading text to apparatus even
more than the previous examples show.

    Using the four guide questions, read this section from a lab manual.
Naturally, you can't follow through and do all that is required now, but
the passage represents a pattern that requires a variety of skills. Explore
it, check the vocabulary, and then read closely.

► ## Exchange and Transport of Materials in Plants[3]

    Water is a universal constituent of protoplasm; for it is in water,
the "universal solvent," that the chemical reactions of organisms
(that is, metabolic activities) take place. Further, all metabolically
important substances are in solution when they diffuse across plasma
membranes. When it is a question of movement of materials, it is

---

[3]DuShane and Regnery, *op. cit.*, pp. 103–108.

convenient to consider the entire plant as a mass of water continuous even through cell walls and membranes. In the lower plants, all substances move from cell to cell by the relatively slow process of diffusion, often combined with cytoplasmic streaming. While these processes remain important in higher plants, the addition of vascular tissue makes possible more rapid transport of water.

A. Passage of Water Into and Out of Cells

1. Osmosis

An apparatus to demonstrate osmosis has been set up on the instructor's table. We shall limit our definition of osmosis to the diffusion of water through a differentially permeable membrane. Inside the cellophane membrane is a solution of large molecules (sugar dissolved in water); outside, is distilled water only. At the beginning of the experiment, the level of the two solutions is the same.

Note the rise in level of the sugar solution. Measure the level every 15 minutes and record the results graphically.

Consider the results in terms of these theoretical and experimental assumptions:

a) Sugar molecules are much larger than water molecules.
b) Sugar molecules do not pass through the membrane into the outside solution.
c) Molecules are in constant random motion at ordinary temperatures.

Given these considerations, can you propose a theory of membrane structure to account for the results? What molecules cross through the membrane in this experiment? How could you set about to prove statement b) above?

2. Plasmolysis

a) **Elodea.** Plasmolysis is the process of shrinkage of protoplasm away from a cell wall as a result of water loss. It is a consequence of osmosis. Put an Elodea leaf into 5% salt solution, and examine it under the microscope. Have the protoplasts (i.e., cells and cell membranes exclusive of the cell walls) shrunk away from the cell walls? Are the cell membranes visible?

Explain these results in terms of osmosis, bearing in mind that a 5% salt solution is much more concentrated, osmotically, than protoplasm.

Wash the leaf and put it into distilled water. Examine again and note the results. Does water cross the plasma membrane? The cell wall?

Treat the cells of a fresh Elodea leaf by adding a strong chemical solution (formalin-acetic acid-alcohol solution). Now try again in the 5% salt solution. Result? Can you explain this change in terms of the cell membrane?

b) **Root Hairs.** In addition to acting as an anchor for the rest of the plant and as a storage organ, the root system has as its function the absorption of water and dissolved mineral salts from the soil. Water and dissolved salts enter the plant through the root hairs. Each root hair is an extension of an epidermal cell. Collectively, the root hairs provide a great surface area through which water and minerals may enter the plant.

Examine a grass seedling showing *root hairs*. Cut off the root of the seedling, and mount it in water under a cover glass. Be sure a portion of the root hair region is included. Study a few epidermal cells showing root hairs. Add a drop of salt solution at the edge of the cover slip. What happens to the root hairs? Explain.

B. Vascular Tissue

1. Root Structure

Although variations in roots are numerous, the fundamental structure of roots is far more uniform than the structure of those parts of the plant above the soil. In a general way, the tissues of the root are similar to those of the stem, and it should be kept in mind that, since these two organs are joined, the tissue systems are continuous from one to the other. Examine a cross-section of the root of a buttercup. It is made up of a central cylinder surrounded by the *cortex*. The outermost layer of cells is the epidermis. Located in the central cylinders of the root is a fluted column (star shaped in cross-section) made up of thick-walled, hollow tubes. These were formed by the end to end fusion of young *xylem* cells, followed by the disintegration of the cross walls and the protoplasm. Lying between the points of the xylem "star" are groups of thin-walled cells, the *phloem* cells. The phloem and the xylem together are referred to as vascular tissue.

2. Stem Structure

The vascular tissue continues into the stem where it separates into individual vascular bundles. This may be demonstrated by immersing the cut stem of a plant in a dye solution. The dye will move up the vascular bundles of the stem and, in favorable circumstances, even into the veins of the leaves. The presence of the dye in the bundles makes it easy to see how they are arranged. Now make longitudinal and cross-sections of these stems. What elements of the vascular bundles contain the dye?

Examine a prepared section of an alfalfa stem, and note that the arrangement of the bundles is similar to that observed above, that is, the bundles are arranged in a ring near the edge of the stem. The large cells in the center of the stem make up the *pith*. Identify the thick-walled xylem vessels next to the pith. Just outside the xylem, find the *cambium*, a continuous ring of small cells whose function will be considered later. Outside the cambium opposite each xylem bundle, find the phloem, a crescentic mass of thin-walled, darkly stained cells.

Such an arrangement of vascular bundles and cambium characterizes a large group of flowering plants known as the *dicotyledons*.

Now examine a prepared section of a corn stem. The rather random arrangement of vascular bundles and the absence of a cambium are characteristic of the *monocotyledons*. The xylem may be readily identified. The phloem cells lie a short distance external to the xylem. The whole bundle is surrounded by small, heavy-walled cells making up the mechanical tissue which gives support to the stem.

C. Transpiration

An apparatus has been set up to demonstrate the loss of water

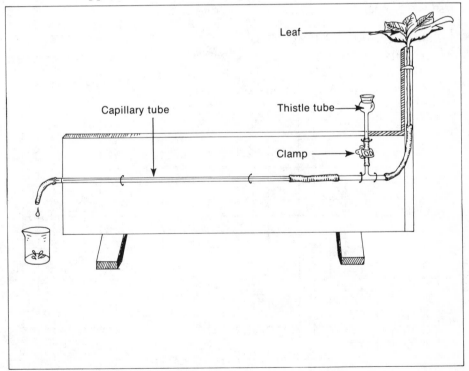

Figure 9.3. Potometer for demonstrating the movement of water in transpiration.

from a plant (*transpiration*). With the apparatus set up as in Figure 9.3, open the stopcock from the reservoir to fill the capillary tube with water. Close the stopcock and note that the column of water moves through the capillary. The rate can thus be measured.

1. *In intact leaves.* Measure the rate of movement of the water column at one minute intervals for five minutes (or less if the column moves rapidly; do not allow the air to pass the point of entry of the reservoir tube). **Graph** the results.

2. *With lower surface of leaves coated.* Repeat the measurements on the same leaves after they have had their upper surfaces coated with petroleum jelly. **Graph** the results.

3. *With both upper and lower surfaces of the leaves coated.* Repeat as above after coating the lower surfaces of the leaves with petroleum jelly. **Graph** the results.

4. Calculate and **record** the percentage rates of transpiration in 1, 2, 3, taking 1 as 100%.

5. Using the high power of the microscope, count the number of stomata visible in the field on the upper surface of the leaf. **Record.** Count the number in the field on the lower surface of the leaf. **Record. Discuss** these counts in relation to transpiration rate.

REPORT: Exp. 16

Exchange and Transport of Materials in Plants

Name _____

Date _____

Section _____

A.1. Graph showing rate of osmosis

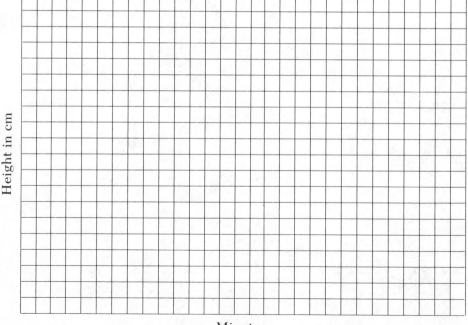

Height in cm

Minutes

C. 1, 2, 3. Transpiration rate under different conditions

Minutes

Discussion Topics

    1. Why is salt added to the soil effective in killing plants?

    2. What is the effect of girdling a dicotyledonous plant (cutting a ring to the depth of the cambium) on the transport of: a) water, b) elaborated foods?

    3. Is transpiration, in general, more rapid by day than by night? Why?

C. 4. Relative rates of transpiration

    1) Intact leaf   <u>100 per cent</u>

    2) Upper surfaces coated   _____

    3) Upper and lower surfaces coated   _____

C. 5. No. of stomata in upper surface (one

        high-power field of the microscope)   _____

    No. of stomata in lower surface (one

        high-power field of the microscope) ◄   _____

Discussion of above data:

Since we have more text and instructions than in previous examples, answer the four questions generally rather than try to be too specific. The point here is to see whether you basically understand the experiment, its purpose, and the directions.

1. The purpose of the experiment is _____

_____

_____

_____

2. The equipment needed is _____

_____

_____

_____

3. The basic steps for performing the experiment are, in order, _____

_____

_____

_____

_____

_____

4. The result(s) is (are) _____

_____

_____

_____

The following answers are, of necessity, general because you are asked to do several experiments throughout this unit. See how close your responses come to the following.

1. The purpose of the experiment is to study and graph the exchange and transport of materials in plants. (Note the title of this unit if you missed this question.)

2. The equipment needed is mostly apparatus already set up for you. But you will need a microscope, a 5% salt solution, formalin-acetic acid-alcohol solution, an Elodea leaf, the root of a buttercup, a dye solution, and a pencil for recording on the graphs.

3. The basic steps for performing the experiments are: 1) Witness osmosis by noting the rise in sugar solution every 15 minutes, record, and answer questions posed; 2) Examine plasmolysis in an Elodea leaf in salt solution under a microscope. Then wash leaf, examine again, and answer questions; 3) Examine plasmolysis in grass seedling root hairs by doing several things; 4) Examine vascular tissue in root structure and stem structure; 5) Follow several recording steps on a graph showing rate of osmosis and transpiration.

Within each of these steps mentioned are several other instructions. Do you at least have the major steps listed?

4. The result can't be found unless you perform the experiment and keep the graphs as directed. But the two major results which would be obtained are the processes of osmosis and transpiration taking place.

SUMMARY

To understand the experiment-instructions pattern, and to make certain you follow the instructions exactly, use these four guide questions:
1. What is the purpose of the experiment?
2. What equipment is needed?
3. What, in order, are the basic steps involved?
4. What are the results?

Because generally you must alternate between the reading matter and the experimental tools, it is necessary to have the four questions firmly in mind before attempting the experiment.

The next time you must read an assignment from your lab manual or read about an experiment in which instructions are given, remember to use the four guide questions for comprehending the experiment-instructions pattern.

Reading the textbook will also help you to do the experiments by giving you a background for observation. If you don't know what to look for, the experiment will have little meaning to you.

10

Analyzing Combinations of Patterns

The total picture. This, the last chapter in Step Three shows you how some of the patterns presented in this step are often combined. For instance, a passage may begin by defining a term but end by describing a process with detailed facts. Thus no one distinct pattern can be recognized because a combination of several patterns was used by the author. For this chapter to be clear, it is necessary that you understand all of the patterns presented so far. You may wish to quickly review all these patterns in your mind or skim the previous chapters in this step. Then explore this chapter before reading closely.

Combining writing patterns

You already know that most writers don't consciously decide on what writing pattern to use before writing. The various patterns exist only because they take form as an author attempts to write what he has to say. So far we have presented five rather common patterns which appear in science textbooks. Remember that these patterns are important only if you can see how the skills needed for reading should be altered to fit the different types of patterns.

It is hoped that eventually the skills you are working on now will become so natural in your everyday reading that you won't have to stop and ask yourself what pattern is being used and how you're supposed to read it. As mentioned in the Introduction, it is the intention of this book to break down the process necessary for the reading of science textbooks so that once you learn it, you can use all the parts as a whole. But to do this you must first learn about the parts of the process.

In this chapter you will see how a combination of the patterns you have studied is often used in scientific writing. To do this, part of a chapter from a science textbook has been reprinted. There are two reasons for this. One reason is an attempt to duplicate what might be an actual science reading assignment. If you can apply what you've learned so far to the "pretend" assignment here, you can do it with any science textbook assignment. The other reason for reprinting almost an entire chapter is that it shows the various patterns mentioned in combination. In effect, it is a rather typical example of an actual reading selection you will encounter in science.

But before you begin the reading assignment, read the sample paragraph below. Taken from the selection you will read later, it is an example of what is meant by the combination pattern.

▶   In the preceding chapter the structure of the leaf was emphasized,. and but a brief mention was made of the functions involved. However, the most important aspect of a study of plants is probably the food manufacturing process (photosynthesis), which occurs primarily in green leaves. This activity of green cells provides the food and the oxygen for all organisms, including animals and non-green plants, as well as the requirements of the plant which itself contains such cells. An organism, such as a green plant, which can manufacture its own foods from simple inorganic substances (usually carbon dioxide and water) is termed an **autotrophe**. Autotrophes are of two types, **photosynthetic** and **chemosynthetic**, which differ in that the former utilize radiant (light) energy and the latter utilize energy derived from chemical reactions (see Chapter 20, especially Section 20.5). Those organisms which cannot manufacture their own food are **heterotrophes**. **Parasites** are those heterotrophes which obtain their food from the living cells or tissues of another organism, while **saprophytes** obtain their food from non-living organic matter (i.e., dead plants and animals, excretions and secretions from plants and animals). Humans are, of course, heterotrophic, just as are all animals and the non-green plants.[1] ◀

Check your understanding of the paragraph pattern by answering the following questions. Do not refer back to the selection.
1. Circle the letters of the patterns you feel are used in combination in the example above.
   a. the classification pattern
   b. the process-description pattern
   c. the factual-statement pattern
   d. the problem-solving pattern
   e. the experiment-instructions pattern
2. Circle the letter of the statement you feel best reflects the main idea

---

[1] Muller, *op. cit.*, p. 104.

of the passage. The main idea of the passage is
   a. to show that humans are heterotrophic.
   b. to classify nutritional types in plants.
   c. to define photosynthesis.
   d. to define photosynthesis and nutritional types.
3. Photosynthesis, as defined here, is _____
_____.
4. The basic difference between *autotrophes* and *heterotrophes* is _____
_____
_____.
5. The two types of autotrophes are
   a. photosynthetic and chemosynthetic.
   b. photosynthetic and heterosynthetic.
   c. parasites and chemosynthetic.
6. The two types of heterotrophes are
   a. parasites and phototrophes.
   b. parasites and saprophytes.
   c. saprophytes and humans.

Compare your answers with these: 1. a and e; 2. d; 3. the food-manufacturing process; 4. autotrophes manufacture their own foods from simple inorganic substances, while heterotrophes cannot manufacture their own food but must obtain food from organic matter; 5. a; 6. b.

If you were able to answer all six questions without referring back to the selection, you had excellent comprehension of the passage. You may wish to skip over much of the following discussion to the next boldface heading. If you had trouble, let the following comments aid you.

The sample passage is concerned primarily with two points—the definition of photosynthesis and the different types of photosynthesis which take place. The author, then, is factually defining and classifying the different types of photosynthesis. The photosynthesis process itself is not explained, though we are told something about it.

The author also defines several terms, each one in relation to its classification, as shown below.

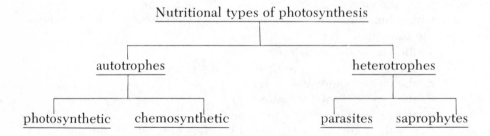

Nutritional types of photosynthesis

autotrophes — heterotrophes

photosynthetic   chemosynthetic   parasites   saprophytes

In addition to this classification, the author contrasts each of the major and minor terms to define them and explain their differences. Notice the contrast in the sentence "Autotrophes are of two types, *photosynthetic* and *chemosynthetic*, which differ in that the former utilize radiant (light) energy and the latter utilize energy derived from chemical reactions. . . ." Also notice that in some cases he even uses examples: ". . . saprophytes obtain their food from non-living organic matter (i.e., dead plants and animals, excretions and secretions from plants and animals)." All these facts and names can be overwhelming unless you are able to see how the author is using them to make major or minor points.

Reading passages that use combinations of patterns may appear difficult at first glance. But if you can sort out the major and minor points through an analysis of the patterns, comprehension will become easier. If you understand the reasons for the responses to the questions you just answered, try the next section. If not, reread the explanation and refer back as needed to the sample passage.

A hypothetical reading assignment

Most of your reading assignments for science classes will be much longer than the short passages used so far. For that reason, we have selected a rather long excerpt that includes visual aids. Pretend it is an actual assignment and do the following:

1. Apply Step One and Step Two to the sample selection.
2. Read the selection carefully, using what you've learned in Step Three.
3. Answer the questions which follow the selection without referring back.

▶ Photosynthesis[2]

Nutritional types

In the preceding chapter the structure of the leaf was emphasized, and but a brief mention was made of the functions involved. However, the most important aspect of a study of plants is probably the food manufacturing process (photosynthesis), which occurs primarily in green leaves. This activity of green cells provides the food and the oxygen for all organisms, including animals and non-green plants, as well as the requirements of the plant which itself contains such cells. An organism, such as a green plant, which can manufacture its own foods from simple inorganic substances (usually carbon dioxide and water) is termed an **autotrophe.** Autotrophes are of two types, **photosynthetic** and **chemosynthetic**, which differ in that the

---

[2]*Ibid.*, pp. 104–108.

former utilize radiant (light) energy and the latter utilize energy derived from chemical reactions (see Chapter 20, especially Section 20.5). Those organisms which cannot manufacture their own food are **heterotrophes. Parasites** are those heterotrophes which obtain their food from the living cells or tissues of another organism, while **saprophytes** obtain their food from non-living organic matter (i.e., dead plants and animals, excretions and secretions from plants and animals). Humans are, of course, heterotrophic, just as are all animals and the non-green plants.

Photosynthesis

The manufacture of food, mainly sugar, from carbon dioxide and water in the presence of chlorophyll, utilizing light energy and releasing oxygen gas, is termed **photosynthesis.*** This process has been under intensive investigation for many years, but the exact mechanisms involved are not yet completely understood. The raw materials and major end products have been known at least since the work of Sachs in the 1860's, but the complexity of the steps between these end points is only now being clarified. Certainly ten or more steps, some of a cyclic nature, are involved.

Essential factors in photosynthesis

Any factor whose presence is required before a reaction proceeds is termed an **essential factor.** This is not a relative term: if any one such factor is absent, the reaction cannot take place. The raw materials, or substrate, of a reaction are essentials, but so also in many instances are certain environmental factors. In photosynthesis the essential factors are: carbon dioxide, water, energy (light), chloroplasts, and a suitable temperature.

Raw materials. Because of the concentration gradient that results from its use as a substrate, carbon dioxide diffuses through the stomata from the atmosphere into the intercellular spaces of the leaf. The content of carbon dioxide in the atmosphere is rather constant at about 0.03 per cent (3 parts per 10,000 parts of air), a seemingly small amount but totalling approximately 2,000,000,000,000 (2×10^{12}) tons in the atmosphere surrounding the earth. This gas is continually being added to the air by the respiration (Chapter 12) of plants and animals, by the decay of organic materials, by the combustion of fuels, by the weathering of rock, and by volcanic activity, although, in fact, the respiration of plants, including micro-organisms,

---

*Some bacteria are photosynthetic but do not utilize water or produce oxygen. The activity of these organisms is insignificantly small in comparison with the green plants.

supplies more carbon dioxide to the atmosphere than comes from all other sources combined. The oceans of the world contain tremendous amounts of dissolved carbon dioxide, probably more than is found in the atmosphere, and act as a great reservoir of this material. Once in the intercellular spaces, the molecules of carbon dioxide dissolve in the water which saturates the walls of the mesophyll cells and diffuse into the cytoplasm and eventually to the chloroplasts of these cells, where photosynthesis takes place.

Water, the other substrate, is absorbed by the roots of the plant and is transported to the leaves through the various cells and tissues as indicated in previous chapters.

Energy. In the synthesis of any material, energy is required in order to convert simple molecules into more complex ones. As the name implies, the energy source in photosynthesis is light energy, with the red and blue wave lengths (colors) being the most effective. The greens and yellows are mainly reflected from and transmitted through the leaf and have much less effect on the process. The sun normally is the source of such radiations, but electric lights can also be used. Only those wave lengths which can be absorbed by chlorophyll are useful in photosynthesis. The process may be considered as one in which radiant energy is converted to chemical energy and stored in the form of the carbohydrate end product—an energy-storing or energy-absorbing process. Even though only about two per cent of the light energy striking a leaf is actually stored in the resultant sugar molecules, the process is more efficient than this would appear to be: most of the light from the sun is reflected, transmitted, or absorbed as heat, but approximately 30 per cent of what is actually absorbed is converted to chemical energy (as sugar).

Pigments. The presence of the green pigment chlorophyll† enables green plants to absorb light energy and to use this energy in the production of sugars. The absorption spectrum for chlorophyll indicates that red and blue wave lengths are absorbed much more than green, and this correlates rather closely with the effect of wave lengths on photosynthesis (see Figure 10.1). Chlorophyll transfers this absorbed energy to the compounds involved in the reaction and also acts as a catalyst.

The **carotenoid** pigments, **xanthophylls** (yellow) and **carotenes** (yellow-orange), are always present in chloroplasts along with the chlorophyll. Recent evidence indicates that such associated pigments, in algae at least, may absorb light and pass this excitation (or energy) to chlorophyll. They may supplement chlorophylls as light

---

†Actually, several chlorophylls (indicated by letters a, b, c, d, e, etc.) have been found, but chlorophyll "a" is the pigment to which the others transfer energy which they have absorbed as light. Green plants contain chlorophylls "a" and "b," whereas the other chlorophylls are present in certain of the algae (see Chapter 19).

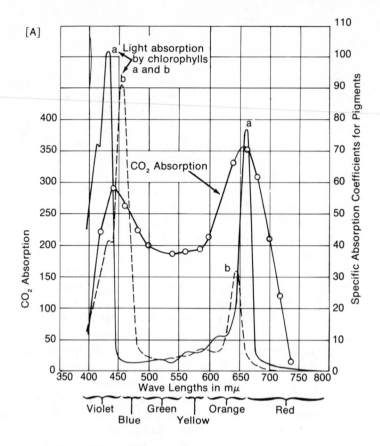

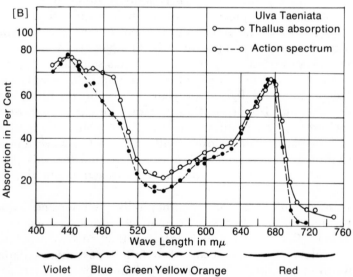

Figure 10.1. Light absorption curves of chlorophyll superimposed on the curve of photosynthetic rate as a function of wavelength of light. A: In wheat plants. (From O. F. Curtis and D. G. Clark, *Introduction to Plant Physiology*. New York: McGraw-Hill. Copyright 1950 by McGraw-Hill, Inc. Used by permission.) B: In *Ulva*, a green alga. (From F. T. Haxo and L. R. Blinks, *Jour. Gen. Physiol.*, 33 (1950), 389–422.)

absorbers, but they are not capable of acting as catalysts in photosynthesis. In higher plants no example of photosynthesis has been found where the cells did not contain chlorophyll. Even those plants that have red leaves are found to contain chlorophyll which is merely masked by the red pigment. Boiling such leaves in water removes the red **anthocyanin,** which is water-soluble and located in the vacuoles of the leaf cells; the green chlorophyll is then visible.

The yellowish pigments are usually not noticed, because they are masked by the color of the chlorophylls and come into prominence only during the fall of the year in many plants. The autumn coloration of many trees results as chlorophyll synthesis decreases while chlorophyll destruction continues. Eventually the carotenes and xanthophylls are no longer hidden; the leaf color changes from green to yellowish, as in the tulip tree (*Liriodendron tulipifera*), elm (*Ulmus*), aspen (*Populus tremuloides*), and hickory (*Carya ovata*). In some trees additional red pigments, anthocyanins, develop, especially if large supplies of carbohydrates are available to the leaves. Red maple (*Acer rubrum*), sumac (*Rhus*), and many oaks (*Quercus*) become quite prominent in the landscape as a result of their dominant red color. As the leaves die, the pigments decompose, and only the brown **tannins** remain. The gorgeous hues of northern forests result from these pigment changes that take place near the end of the growing season. Frost does not bring about this coloration. In fact, early frosts tend to decrease the color display, especially with regard to the red pigments, by bringing about the early death of leaves and the rapid appearance of the brown tannins. However, exceptionally brilliant autumn coloration usually occurs if fairly low night temperatures, which retard the removal of food from leaves, are associated with bright sunny days, which favor photosynthesis and sugar production.

Temperature. Photosynthesis generally takes place over a range of temperature from 5 to 40°C., the rate increasing as the temperature rises, up to approximately 35°C., after which a rapid decline in rate occurs. This decrease in rate is probably due to enzyme inactivation at the higher temperatures. Since the process is influenced by temperature as well as by light, it is apparent that both chemical and photo-chemical reactions are involved because the latter are independent of temperature. This will be discussed more fully later. The enzymes that are involved have not all been identified, but the evidence for their presence is quite conclusive. More refined techniques will undoubtedly clarify this situation in the future.

Additional essential factors. Present in chloroplasts, along with the pigments already mentioned, are various carrier molecules whose functions have only recently been elucidated. They are important in transferring hydrogen atoms and in transferring energy. These activities are discussed in more detail in Section 10.6 ◄

Comprehension Check. Answer the following questions without referring back to the selection. Fill in the best correct response.

_____ 1. The two basic nutritional types are
   a. photosynthetic and chemosynthetic.
   b. parasites and saprophytes.
   c. autotrophes and heterotrophes.

_____ 2. Photosynthesis is best defined as
   a. the food-manufacturing process in living organisms.
   b. the manufacture of food (mainly sugar), by which carbon dioxide, present in chlorophyll, utilizes light energy and releases oxygen gas.
   c. the manufacture of food (mainly sugar), from carbon dioxide and water in the presence of chlorophyll, utilizing light energy and releasing oxygen gas.

_____ 3. Which of the following items is *not* an essential factor in photosynthesis?
   a. carbon dioxide   c. energy   e. suitable temperature
   b. water   d. chloroplasts   f. photogen

_____ 4. An *essential factor*, as defined in the text, is
   a. a factor whose presence is required before a reaction can proceed.
   b. a factor necessary to releasing chloroplasts in the correct quantity and dimension.
   c. a factor of environment.

_____ 5. The content of carbon dioxide in the atmosphere is
   a. about 3 parts per 100,000 parts of air.
   b. 2×10^{12} tons in the atmosphere surrounding the earth.
   c. not important in connection with photosynthesis.

_____ 6. The most important source of carbon dioxide in the atmosphere is
   a. volcanic activity.   c. the respiration of plants.
   b. the decay of plants and animals.

_____ 7. The energy for photosynthesis is supplied from
   a. plant leaves.   b. light.   c. chlorophyll.

_____ 8. Figure 10.1 shows the absorption spectrum for chlorophyll and indicates that_____ and _____ wavelengths are absorbed best.
   a. green and red   b. red and blue   c. blue and green

_____ 9. T or F: Red leaves do not contain chlorophyll.

_____ 10. The autumn coloration of many trees results from
   a. frost decreasing the color display.
   b. low temperature.
   c. chlorophyll synthesis decreasing while chlorophyll destruction continues.

Compare your answers with the following: 1. c; 2. c; 3. f; 4. a; 5. b; 6. c; 7. b; 8. b; 9. F; 10. c. If you scored 80 percent or more on the 10 questions, you have a firm grasp of the passage's main points and some minor ones besides. You may wish to skim over the next section, looking only for things you don't know or understand about the combination pattern. However, if the questions gave you trouble, read the next section carefully.

Analyzing combinations of patterns

A closer look at the sample textbook passage you just read may help to clarify the reading approach necessary for understanding such passages. Since the first paragraph was explicated for you before you began reading the sample selection, skip it and reread the second paragraph quickly.

The main idea in this paragraph is to define photosynthesis through factual statements. That is precisely what the first sentence does. The author even footnotes his definition to answer any reader who may wish to challenge the definition on one minor point. Then the author gives you some minor facts: the complete process is not totally understood; part of the process has been known since 1860; and 10 or more steps (some cyclic) are involved. Thus the basic pattern is factual definition, as you were shown in Chapter 7.

Now quickly reread the paragraph under the subheading "Raw Materials." Can you see the difference here where a combination of patterns is used? The first four sentences are factual statements revealing that:

1. Carbon dioxide diffuses through the stomata from the atmosphere into the intercellular spaces of the leaf.

2. Carbon dioxide in the atmosphere is rather constant at about 0.03 percent (3 parts per 10,000 parts of air) or 2,000,000,000,000 (2×10^{12}) tons.

3. The gas is added to the air by respiration of plants and animals, combustion of fuels, weathering of rock, and volcanic activity.

4. Oceans act as carbon-dioxide reservoirs.

But then the author switches from factual statements to a description of the process in which molecules of carbon dioxide dissolve in water, and we get something like this:

molecules of carbon dioxide enter intercellular spaces
⬇
molecules then dissolve in the water of the mesophyll cells
⬇
molecules then diffuse into the cytoplasm
⬇
eventually molecules diffuse into the chloroplasts of the mesophyll cells ⬇
photosynthesis takes place in the chloroplasts of the mesophyll cells

Thus, in one passage, the author uses both the factual-statement pattern and the process-description pattern. But again notice that recognizing the pattern is not the purpose of this analysis. Recognizing the pattern's structure helps you organize the points being made in the passage.

Now quickly reread the section under the heading "Energy." There are two major points or ideas being presented here, each one through a different writing pattern. In the space below, comment on what you think the two major points are and what two patterns you think are used to present them.

Here again the author uses a combination of the factual-statement and process-description patterns. Two points are being made. One is a statement of fact: energy is required in any type of synthesis to convert simpler molecules into more complex ones. The other point is how the process of light energy works: red and blue wavelengths are absorbed by chlorophyll, and radiant energy is converted to chemical energy. The entire paragraph is a mixture of factual statement and process description. However, the process is not presented on a highly technical level.

Turn back to the sample selection again, this time to the first paragraph under the section "Pigments." Can you recognize the basic pattern? Probably it's best classified as factual statement, with one difference. You are referred to Figure 10-1. Reading this figure might be called the classification pattern because it classifies light-absorption curves of chlorophyll superimposed on the curve of photosynthetic rate as a function of wavelength of light both in wheat plants [A] and in a green alga [B].

Using Figure 10-1 as a guide, answer these questions:
1. Which chlorophyll absorbed the most CO_2? _____
2. Which chlorophyll absorbed the most light? _____
3. What is chlorophyll "b"? _____
4. What is the highest absorption of CO_2 in chlorophyll "b"? _____
   _____; the lowest? _____
5. What wavelength (color) has the lowest effect on the Ulva? _____
   _____; the highest? _____

The answers are 1. a; 2. a; 3. a wheat plant chlorophyll; 4. 455 at 450 mμ, 0 at 750 mμ; 5. green, violet. The combination of facts and processes is utilized here.

If you were to analyze the total sample selection, you might call it a combination of factual detail, classification, and process description. Failure to adapt your reading approach to these different patterns could result in haphazard or random comprehension of the material. But an awareness of these patterns can guide your thinking process to coincide with the writing pattern of the author. Reading *is* a thinking process. By now you are aware of this.

SUMMARY

In this last chapter of Step Three, you are shown how some of the patterns already discussed in previous chapters are often combined. Science textbook passages may use two or more patterns. For instance, a reading passage may begin with a factual statement of definition, move to classifying the components or parts of the term being classified, and end up discussing a process. Such a combination is not difficult to read if you are able to identify the main point of the statements.

An awareness of the pattern has been stressed in this step, not for the sake of learning patterns, but rather for the sake of helping you adjust your reading skills to distinguish the main ideas and supporting details in the various patterns used.

You may wish to do the exercises on pages 215–219 in the practices section before going on to Step Four.

FOUR

Synthesize for Understanding

To synthesize means to combine separate parts to make a whole. In this last step you will put together what you learned in the first three.

This section is divided into four chapters. Each chapter is part of the synthesizing process. Chapter 11 shows you how some students take notes and helps you devise your own system for "reading with a pen." Chapter 12 discusses the sources which are available in a library for science students. Chapter 13 gives you some suggestions for taking tests. Finally, Chapter 14 discusses the most important aspect of reading the sciences —connecting what you read with your own experiences and needs.

Before you begin the last step, be sure you understand the first three. Take the time to answer the following questions.

1. Define *exploring*.

2. Define what is meant by *check the vocabulary*.

3. Define *analysis*, as discussed throughout Step Three.

If you aren't able to give good, clear answers that deal with each step specifically, then do some reviewing before going on. If you understand the first three steps, you are ready to begin putting the parts together.

11

Taking Notes

The total picture. It's one thing to be able to read quickly and well; it's quite another to be able to remember what you read. Remember the final exam you took last semester in your history class? The chances are small that you could pass it today. Most students, even so-called "A students," don't read to remember much longer than it takes to pass a test. Taking good notes is a way to help you remember what you read, not only for a test, but much longer. If you don't take notes as you read, or if you take poor notes, you're actually making learning much harder than it need be. Two ways to improve your note-taking habits are discussed in this chapter.

Explore this chapter before you read it closely.

Two ways to take notes

As a college student, you've probably already discovered that there are two basic tools for taking notes. Either you write in the textbook (if it is yours) making comments in the margins and marking important words and phrases, or you take notes in a notebook.

Marking in textbooks or taking notes as you read is important for several reasons: (1) It helps you keep your mind on what you are reading. (2) Paying close attention as you read will result in longer retention if you connect it to what you already know. (3) Good notes are helpful for review. (4) If you mark correctly, not only will you connect the author's ideas with your own, but you will also have a record of your thoughts and reactions.

You're probably thinking "I already know how to do all that." Maybe you do, but it might pay you to take a look at the following example of how one student marked his text.

▶ A puzzling group of Cambrian organisms, the **Archaeocyatha** (ancient cups), were the earliest known reef-forming animals. They left conical calcareous fossils up to 4 inches long. Although they resemble both sponges and corals, they are sufficiently different to merit being included in a phylum by themselves. Archaeocyathids had very wide distribution, being especially abundant in Australia and Siberia. Their fossils gave the first clues to the presence of Cambrian rocks in Antarctica. The group is confined almost entirely to the Early Cambrian. So far as is known, this is the first phylum to become extinct.

Trilobites make up about 60 per cent of all Cambrian fossils. Brachiopods constitute 10 to 20 per cent; and the remainder includes archaeocyathids, protozoans, sponges, worms, gastropods, echinoderms such as cystoids, cephalopods, and arthopods other than trilobites. The trilobites and brachiopods so completely dominate the Cambrian fossil record that all other forms are interesting chiefly for the information they yield about the primitive beginnings of their respective lines. Among the groups not yet found in Cambrian rocks are bone-bearing animals, **pelecypods, bryozoans, true corals, starfish, and sea urchins.**[1] ◄

How helpful are all these marks? What do they all mean? What good will they be to the person who marked them when it is time to review for a test? The reason for marking is to aid comprehension and memory. This sort of marking only clutters up the page.

Marking your book

While there are no official rules for note-taking, you do need to set up some rules for yourself so that six or eight weeks or even a year after you have marked a book, the marks will still mean something. Notice how, in the following example, the same passage on Cambrian organisms has been marked differently. Do these marks seem to be more useful than those in the passage above?

Def.

Descrip.

Location

▶ A puzzling group of Cambrian organisms, the **Archaeocyatha** (ancient cups), were the earliest known reef-forming animals. They left conical calcareous fossils up to 4 inches long. Although they resemble both sponges and corals, they are sufficiently different to merit being included in a phylum by themselves. Archaeocyathids had very wide distribution, being especially abundant in Australia and Siberia. Their fossils gave the first clues to the presence of Cambrian rocks in Antartica.

---

[1]Stokes, *op. cit.*, p. 195.

The group is confined almost entirely to the Early Cambrian. So far as is known, this is the first phylum to become extinct.

Trilobites make up about 60 per cent of all Cambrian fossils. Brachiopods constitute 10 to 20 per cent; and the remainder includes archaeocyathids, protozoans, sponges, worms, gastro- *minor* pods, echinoderms such as cystoids, cephalopods, and artho- pods other than trilobites. The trilobites and brachiopods so completely dominate the Cambrian fossil record that all other forms are interesting chiefly for the information they yield about the primitive beginnings of their respective lines. Among the groups not yet found in Cambrian rocks are bone-bearing animals, **pelecypods, bryozoans, true corals, starfish,** and **sea urchins.**[2] ◄

3 major classifications of Cambrian fossils

The markings on this passage are more useful because they highlight the main points and help the reader organize the material. Using Step Three: *Analyze for Comprehension,* the reader discovered that the passage is using both a classification pattern and a definition-by-factual-statement pattern. The reader saw that the main point is a classification of Cambrian fossils. The Archaeocyatha are the oldest of the Cambrian organisms. They are defined (ancient cups), described, and given a location. Then further classification takes place, and the reader sees that there are three major types of Cambrian fossils: Trilobites, brachiopods, and archaeocyathids, and a lot of other minor types. The reader also noted that while the Archaeocyatha are given importance in the selection, the trilobites and brachiopods dominate the Cambrian fossil record.

Analyzing the paragraph in this way, using Step Three, gives the reader a framework for what he is reading. If it is marked according to analysis, the reader can review the passage quickly by skimming and still retain the essence of the passage.

To repeat, there is no one way of marking which is best for everyone. After all, the markings are for your own benefit, but they must be meaningful to you as you read and learn and when you review. All good note-takers do seem to follow two basic principles: (1) mark only key points or facts; (2) be consistent in the meaning of your marks.

Here are some suggestions that might help you develop a key for marking your books. Try them or devise some which will work best for you.

1. Use a pen, not a pencil. If you prefer pencils, then use them, but pencil marks fade and smear after a while. Make sure the ink color will stand out clearly. Red is a good color to use.

2. Underline the main ideas in a paragraph; circle important words or phrases; draw boxes around the names of persons or places that seem important.

---

[2] *Ibid.,* p. 195.

3. Put a check mark in the margin next to any important statement that is opinion rather than fact.

4. Underline minor but important facts or statistics with broken lines.

5. Use numbers or letters in the margin to indicate chronology or a series of items.

6. Use the margins to write in anything that you feel will be important to you in the future. As you read, questions you can't answer may pop into your head. Write them in the book so that you will remember to ask the instructor for the answer. Or use the margins to write your personal reaction to what's being said.

7. Note page numbers where related subjects are discussed in the text.

Remember, don't feel that you *must* use all or any of these marks. Whatever marks you use must make sense to you. If you don't feel that those mentioned are really necessary, don't use them. Here is an example, however, of how you might use the above suggestions.

►   Another form of energy, quite different from potential, is the energy of moving bodies. It is called *kinetic energy*. A ball rolling on the table top has no potential energy with respect to the table top, yet it has energy because it is moving. What gives it this energy? Obviously the energy comes from motion, for the ball has no energy when it is standing still. But what aspect of its motion? A little analysis or experimentation reveals that one of the factors is the *speed*. Thus a bullet thrown at us leisurely would not worry us, but the bullet coming toward us with a speed of 2000 feet per second would be another matter. The difference between the two cases is speed. The other factor in the kinetic energy is the *mass* of the moving body. If a toy train is coming toward us with a speed of 3 feet per second (about 2 miles per hour), it would cause no concern. But if a real locomotive is coming toward us with the same speed, we had better step aside. What is the difference? The real locomotive has a much greater mass. Thus, the kinetic energy of a moving body depends on the *mass* and on the *speed*.[3] ◄

example

example

2 factors in Kinetic energy

Notice that not everything in this passage is marked. Only those items that summarize or reflect the main points are marked, with some comments added by the reader. This shows active reading. The reader was looking beyond the words to the ideas. He was connecting or synthesizing what he read. The next time he looks over the marked pages, he can explore quickly. He can recall the main points, as well as his reactions to them.

---

[3]Ashford, *op. cit.*, p. 86.

From the text to your notebook

The alternative to making notes in your book is to write them down in a notebook. There are many times when you have to use this technique — for example, when you are using books that don't belong to you. But you may also want to use this method because you prefer keeping your notes together or because you want to sell your textbook when the course is over. At any rate, writing notes forces you to rephrase the author's ideas in your own words, and this means you have to understand what you read.

There is no one right way to write out your notes. However, here are a few guidelines for you to consider when making notes from your textbook.

1. Always put down the title of the book, the title of the chapter, and the numbers of the pages your notes cover.

2. Write the main ideas of the passage as your major headings and list the minor ideas or facts under them.

3. Let the writing pattern of the author help you write your notes. If he defines a term, be sure your notes contain a good definition of the term. If he compares or contrasts two things, be sure your notes compare or contrast them. If he is classifying, your notes might contain outlines such as those shown in Chapter 5.

4. Make certain you avoid copying the exact wording used in the text. Write the notes in your own words. A good test of how well you know something is how well you can say it in your own words.

5. Make a list of the words you don't know so that you can look them up later. If you have trouble with your notes because the vocabulary is unfamiliar, look up the words as you write your notes.

Here is a sample. Read it and then notice on p. 172 the way one student wrote his notes.

►   The graptolites were another group of colonial animals that became common in the Ordovician. Some types were fixed like small shrubs to the sea bottom, and others floated freely in the upper levels or were attached to seaweeds. They are extinct, and we know very little about their relationships to other animals. Their skeletons were composed of **chitinous** material and were light enough to float but too thin to afford much protection. Graptolites existed in many forms and went through distinctive evolutionary stages during the Ordovician and Silurian.

The **cephalopods** (described in greater detail in Chapter 20) also flourished during the Ordovician. Their variously shaped chambered shells were buoyant enough to permit the animals to move about rapidly, and their keen senses probably made them the most advanced of all marine invertebrates.

Another group, the **crinoids,** also began to leave an abundant fossil record during the Ordovician. Crinoids are echinoderms with plant-like stems and roots and a flower-like crown or head. The stem enabled the animals to keep their food-collecting devices well above the ocean bottom, but they were delicate affairs and could easily be broken. Complete crinoid specimens are rare. Their heads are composed of many calcite plates that usually fall apart. The most common remains are the round, flat, disc-like structures that make up the stem.[4] ◄

Here is a sample passage for you to mark.

►   In many ways the Cenozoic was markedly different from preceding eras. (1) It was much shorter, only 60 million years compared with 170 million years for the Mesozoic and 370 million for the Paleozoic. (2) It was a time when the continents stood for the most part well above sea level. No longer did shallow seas spread widely; in North America, marine beds are found only in narrow strips along the Pacific Coast and on the Atlantic Coast from New Jersey south to Yucatan. The locally thick Tertiary beds east and west of the Rocky Mountains are river, lake, and wind deposits made in continental basins. (3) Climates during much of the Cenozoic had a diversity like those of the present: the distribution of plants and animals shows that, instead of having widespread moderate climates like those of other eras, Cenozoic continents had zones of distinct hot, cold, humid, and dry climates.

A fourth characteristic of Cenozoic times was widespread volcanic activity. From the Rockies to the Pacific Coast lava flows and tuff beds testify to the former presence of volcanoes, some of which have only recently become extinct. In the mid-Tertiary, immense flows of basalt inundated an area of nearly 200,000 square miles in Oregon, Idaho, and Washington; some of these flows today form the somber cliffs of the Columbia River gorge.

Finally, the Cenozoic was a time of almost continuous diastrophic disturbance, in contrast to the long periods of crustal stability in previous eras. Movements associated with the Rocky Mountain revolution lasted well into the Tertiary. In mid-Tertiary the Alps and Carpathians of Europe and the Himalayas of Asia were folded and uplifted. Toward the end of the Tertiary the Cascade range of Washington and Oregon was formed, and other mountain-building movements began around the border of the Pacific which have continued to the present day. Mountain ranges that had been folded earlier—the Appalachians, the Rockies, the Sierra Nevada—were repeatedly uplifted during

[4]Stokes, *op. cit.*, p. 199.

the Cenozoic, and erosion following these uplifts has shaped their present topography.[5] ◄

Now compare your marking of the passage with the following. Yours does not have to be like this one, of course, but at least you should have noted the important points marked below.

►   In many ways the Cenozoic was markedly different from preceding eras. (1) It was much shorter, only 60 million years compared with 170 million years for the Mesozoic and 370 million for the Paleozoic. (2) It was a time when the continents stood for the most part well above sea level. No longer did shallow seas spread widely; in North America, marine beds are found only in narrow strips along the Pacific Coast and on the Atlantic Coast from New Jersey south to Yucatan. The locally thick Tertiary beds east and west of the Rocky Mountains are river, lake, and wind deposits made in continental basins. (3) Climates during much of the Cenozoic had a diversity like those of the present: the distribution of plants and animals shows that, instead of having widespread moderate climates like those of other eras, Cenozoic continents had zones of distinct hot, cold, humid, and dry climates.

Five factual comparison/ contrast statements

A fourth characteristic of Cenozoic times was widespread volcanic activity. From the Rockies to the Pacific Coast lava flows and tuff beds testify to the former presence of volcanoes, some of which have only recently become extinct. In the mid-Tertiary, immense flows of basalt inundated an area of nearly 200,000 square miles in Oregon, Idaho, and Washington; some of these flows today form the somber cliffs of the Columbia River gorge.

Finally, the Cenozoic was a time of almost continuous diastrophic disturbance, in contrast to the long periods of crustal stability in previous eras. Movements associated with the Rocky Mountain revolution lasted well into the Tertiary. In mid-Tertiary the Alps and Carpathians of Europe and the Himalayas of Asia were folded and uplifted. Toward the end of the Tertiary the Cascade range of Washington and Oregon was formed, and other mountain-building movements began around the border of the Pacific which have continued to the present day. Mountain ranges that had been folded earlier—the Appalachians, the Rockies, the Sierra Nevada—were repeatedly up-

lifted during the Cenozoic, and erosion following these uplifts
has shaped their present topography.[6] ◄

Now try your hand at writing down notes from the same passage.
Use p. 186 for note-taking if space provided is not sufficient.

Compare your notes with the ones that follow. Again they don't have to
be exactly the same.

Remember, there is no single right way to take notes. But as you take
notes, be sure that the marking and writing you do help you learn. Don't
just mark items or write notes without first understanding what it is you're
noting.

You can check the effectiveness of your note-taking by comparing your
reading notes with your lecture notes and with your test results. Some
students write their lecture notes alongside their reading notes. Lectures
and tests tend to concentrate on the important points.

SUMMARY

Note-taking — whatever way you choose to do it — is the best way to put
all four steps of this book into practice. Here are the main reasons:

1. Marking books or taking notes forces you to concentrate on what
you are reading and to look for important points.

2. If you are really paying attention to what you're reading, you will be
surprised at how much you can remember without deliberately memorizing it.

3. Marking correctly can be helpful when you review. Instead of re-
reading entire chapters or scanning haphazardly, you will be able to find
the important sections easily.

4. Writing your personal comments as you read will help you connect
the author's ideas with your own knowledge. You'll also have a record of
your thoughts and reactions.

You will find more exercises to help you on pages 221–225 in the practices section.

---

[6]*Ibid.*, pp. 578–579.

Notice that the author, title, location, and page number appear first. Did you do this?

Krauskopf and Beiser, Fundamentals of Physical Science, McGraw-Hill, 1966, Chapter 36, pp. 518-579.

Covers the main point of the passage.

Basic idea is, to define the Cenozoic era by contrasting it with preceding eras.

Five major differences stressed.

Notice the use of numbers to make the five differences distinct.

Differences from preceding eras:

1. Shorter- only 60-million-year period (Mesozoic 170- Paleozoic 370).

2. Continents stood above sea level (no shallow seas).

3. Diverse climates similar to present (distinct zones - hot, cold, humid; plant and animal remains show this).

4. Widespread volcanic activity, Rockies to Pacific coast.

Notice examples of diastrophic disturbance listed.

5. Diastrophic disturbances as opposed to crustal stability.

    a. Rocky Mountains

    b. Alps and Carpathians

    c. Himalayas

    d. Appalachians

    e. Sierra Nevada

12

Using Outside Reading Sources

The total picture. As a part of Step Four: *Synthesize for Understanding*, this chapter shows you ways to connect what you read and hear in class with outside reading sources. It introduces you to useful publications and references dealing with the sciences. It also shows you how to get started on a term paper and how to fill out the reading-card reports that are required by some instructors. If you are familiar with the contents of this chapter, you may want to skip or skim over it. But be certain you know what the chapter is presenting before you move on.

Explore this chapter before you read closely.

Reading beyond the textbook

Some books are dated as soon as they are published. Your science textbook, even if it bears this year's copyright date, is dated. This doesn't mean the book is not correct, merely that it is not current. Most of the information you read in first-year science courses is fairly standard and deals with material that has been proved. However, scientists are always investigating and experimenting. New discoveries are being made and old ideas challenged every day.

One science textbook can't contain everything in its field. Science writers must select what they feel are the most fundamental areas. This means that author *A* may want his science book to deal with contemporary fields of interest. He will cover historical and less contemporary scientific knowledge quickly in order to devote more space to the present trends of science. Author *B*, on the other hand, may wish to give the most emphasis to the bodies of knowledge least likely to be challenged in the near future. Thus we find textbooks, no matter how good, not covering everything you or your instructors want to cover. That's where outside reading sources come in handy.

Your science instructor may give you a list of good references for outside reading. Or he may feel that it is your job to become familiar with the resources available. Would you know where to begin looking or what is available? In the space below, list the science references with which you are familiar:

A. *Magazines and journals*   B. *Reference books*

    _____   _____
    _____   _____
    _____   _____
    _____   _____
    _____   _____

If you could fill in the blanks with appropriate publications, you're in good shape. The magazines most people know are *Life, Time, Newsweek, Playboy,* and *Look.* Each of these magazines has some value within its own frame of reference, and they generally contain articles or features dealing with some aspects of science. However, their coverage often lacks any depth. They may be fun to read, but there are better sources. Most students are aware of the *Encyclopaedia Britannica, World Book, Compton's Encyclopedia,* and the other standard encyclopedias. But few students are familiar with encyclopedias dealing only with various aspects of science.

Here is a list of publications, some of which you may have listed above. You might want to look over this list and then check to see whether your school library has them.

A. General works dealing with science
    1. *The American Yearbook: A Record of Events and Progress*
    2. *A Century of Progress in the Natural Sciences: 1853–1953*
    3. *Applied Science and Technology Index*
    4. *Chamber's Dictionary of Scientists*
    5. *Dictionary of Scientific Terms.* One book each in Biology, Botany, Zoology, Anatomy, Cytology, Genetics, Embryology, and Physiology.
    6. *McGraw-Hill Encyclopedia of Science and Technology*
    7. *Science Reference Sources*
    8. *Science Abstracts*
    9. *Van Nostrand's Scientific Encyclopedia*
B. Biology sources
    1. *Agricultural Index*
    2. *Biological Abstracts*
    3. *Encyclopedia of the Biological Sciences*

4. *Handbook of Biological Data*
5. *A Short History of Biology*
C. Chemistry sources
   1. *Chemical Abstracts*
   2. *Guide to the Literature of Chemistry*
   3. *Encyclopedia of Chemical Technology*
   4. *Handbook of Chemistry and Physics*
   5. *Van Nostrand's Chemical Annual*
D. Geology sources
   1. *Geological Abstracts*
   2. *Field Book of Common Rocks and Minerals*
   3. *Guide to Geological Literature*
   4. *Minerals Year Book*
E. Physics sources
   1. *Dictionary of Applied Physics*
   2. *Handbook of Chemistry and Physics*
   3. *Reviews of Modern Physics*
   4. *Glossary of Physics*
F. Journals and periodicals in science
   1. *Advancement of Science*
   2. *American Journal of Anatomy*
   3. *American Journal of Botany*
   4. a. *American Scientist*
      b. *American Naturalist*
      c. *American Zoologist*
   5. *Annals and Magazine of Natural History*
   6. *Applied Microbiology*
   7. *Audubon Magazine*
   8. *Biochemistry Journal*
   9. *Bioscience*
 10. *Bulletin of Aquatic Biology*
 11. *Bulletin of the Atomic Scientists*
 12. *Ecology*
 13. *General Science Quarterly*
 14. *Journal of Animal Behavior*
 15. *Journal of Bacteriology*
 16. *Journal of Ecology*
 17. *Journal of Geology*
 18. *Journal of Paleontology*
 19. *Journal of Physiology*
 20. *National Wildlife*
 21. *Naturalist*
 22. *Nature*
 23. *Sea Frontiers*
 24. *Science*

25. *Science News*
26. *Scientific American*
27. *Scientific American Monthly*
28. *Scientific Monthly*
29. *Soil Conservation*
30. *Undersea Technology*

These are only a few of the publications available in any good library. Also, most of the works listed contain bibliographies, thus opening up more references that may be useful. Make it a point to find some of these references in your library and look through them. Later, if you're working on a term project or research paper, your familiarity with the various references will be helpful.

In the stacks of your library you will also find hundreds of books dealing with all aspects of science. Any time you're in a mood to explore, the stacks will be a good place to start.

If your library uses the Dewey decimal system of classifying books, the numbers for the sciences are 500 to 599, broken down as follows:

500–509 pure science
510–519 mathematics
520–529 astronomy
530–539 physics
540–549 chemistry
550–559 geology
560–569 paleontology
570–579 biology
580–589 botany
590–599 zoology

Not all libraries use this classification system. The other widely used plan is the Library of Congress system. If your library is not arranged according to the Dewey decimal system, you will find science listed under books featured with the capital letter *Q* followed by numbers.

How to use outside sources

How you read in sources outside your textbook will depend on why you are reading them. You may need to read in outside sources for a research paper, or you may just be reading to fulfill reading-card assignments like those in the sample Biology I study-guide sheet mentioned in Chapter 1 (see page 4). The latter, of course, may not require the research or intense reading that a reasearch paper demands.

Imagine for a moment that you are in the library doing research for a project on weight control or obesity. You've decided you want to find some articles on the topic to go along with some books you've checked out.

Under *Obesity* in the *Readers' Guide to Periodical Literature* you would find the following:

▶   OBESITY. See Corpulence[1] ◀
This refers you to another listing:

▶   CORPULENCE
Determinants of food intake in obesity. R. E. Nisbett. bibliog il Science 159:1254–5 Mr 15 '68
How to stop regaining weight after dieting. J. C. G. Conniff. il Ladies Home J 85:84+ Ap '68
Who should be fat. Sci Digest 63:76–7 Ap '68
Anecdotes, facetiae, satire, etc.
Notes from the overfed. W. Allen. New Yorker 44:38–9 Mr 16 '68[2] ◀

Of all the listings, the one from the March 15, 1968 *Science* sounds more technical than the others. Turning to page 1254, as the *Readers' Guide* indicated, you find the article "Determinants of Food Intake in Obesity."

For your convenience, the article is reproduced for you on the next few pages. Use the article to practice the reading skills you have learned in this book, particularly the skills of marking and taking notes. Naturally, you should never mark up a book, journal, or magazine that belongs to the library, but this article is printed here for you to write on. Ordinarily, if an article is one you need to take home with you for further work, you can have the library duplicate it on a photocopy machine. Most libraries have such machines.

Here are general suggestions for reading an article for which you need good comprehension. They incorporate the basic steps of this book.

STEP I   Explore the article before reading it all the way through, as you learned in Chapter 2. (Under actual conditions, the article might not suit your purpose.) Notice the subheadings, if any, and use them as guides for understanding the main ideas.

---

[1]From *Readers' Guide*, Vol. 68, No. 6 (May 10, 1968), 88. Copyright 1968 by the H. W. Wilson Company.
[2]*Ibid.*, p. 88.

Look at the visual aids and note how they are related to the title of the article. Of course, they will make more sense after you read closely. If the article looks like one you can use, make the following notes on an index card or in your notebook:

1. Write down the author's name, title of article, the name and date of the journal, and page numbers.
2. State the general thesis or main idea of the article.
3. List the subheadings, leaving space for notes between them.

STEP II   Check the vocabulary.

1. Underline any words you don't fully understand. If necessary, look them up in the dictionary.
2. Write the definitions of these words in the margins.
3. Put a wavy line under any word that shows bias of the author or is a word to remember. Later you may wish to make a vocabulary card for unfamiliar words, as shown in Chapter 4.

STEP III   Analyze the article carefully now, paragraph by paragraph if necessary for good comprehension, and make the following notes as you do:

1. Underline the key sentence or main idea in each paragraph.
2. Circle any words which are clues or guides to you, such as *for example, on the contrary, in comparison, nevertheless, thus.* These words signal that changes, examples, or summaries are about to appear.
3. Summarize the basic ideas of each section of the article under the subheading on your index card or in your notebook.
4. Place a question mark in the margin beside any sentence that states something you don't believe is true, or don't fully understand.

STEP IV   Synthesize your ideas. On the index card, or in your notes, do the following:

1. Summarize in your own words what you have learned from the article.
2. Write down what you think is fact and what is opinion.
3. Write down questions needing further thought.
4. Jot down references to other articles dealing with the subject or to the names of people or organizations you should learn more about. These can be taken from footnotes or bibliographies following the article.

Now apply these steps as a total process to the following article. Questions follow the article so that you may check to see how well you followed the four steps.

► Determinants of Food Intake in Obesity[3]

Richard E. Nisbett

Abstract. *Obese human subjects who were offered three sandwiches ate more than normal subjects. When only one sandwich was offered and additional sandwiches were available but out of sight, the obese subjects ate less than normal subjects. This result is discussed in terms of the types of cues that motivate eating for obese versus normal individuals.*

Recent work by Schachter (*1*) and his colleagues has demonstrated that the factors that govern an individual's eating behavior are related to his weight, that is, weight controlling for height. This work may be summarized by two generalizations: (i) The more an individual weighs, the less responsive he is to internal physiological cues indicative of nutritional state, and (ii) the more an individual weighs, the more responsive he is to external food- or environment-related cues.

Evidence in support of the first proposition includes a study by Stunkard and Koch (*1a*) in which a strong correspondence between extent of gastric motility and verbal reports of hunger was found for normal subjects and a much weaker correspondence for obese subjects. Schachter *et al.* (*2*) found that obese subjects ate no more food after being deprived for several hours than they did after being recently fed, while normal subjects ate much more food after they had been deprived. Goldman *et al.* (*3*) observed that obese individuals were less discomfited by enforced deprivation and altered eating schedules than normal individuals were.

The second proposition is supported by the finding of Schachter and Gross (*4*) that obese subjects ate more when they were persuaded by a speeded-up clock to believe that it was dinnertime, but this was not true for normal subjects. Nisbett (*5*) reported that overweight subjects ate far more good-tasting ice cream than ice cream adulterated with quinine, while normal subjects were less affected by the difference in taste; underweight subjects were still less affected.

If it is true that overweight individuals respond to external rather than to internal cues, it should be possible to control the amount of food they eat by varying the number of external cues that encourage eating. The most direct way to manipulate the number of external cues is simply to vary the amount of food presented to subjects. Consider the behavior we would expect of an individual who is deprived

•

[3]From *Science*, Vol. 159, No. 3820 (March 15, 1968), 1254–1255. Copyright 1968 by the American Association for the Advancement of Science.

and then offered a small meal. If he is not obese, his sensitivity to internal state will motivate him to obtain more food. If it is available, he will eat more than the small amount he was offered. If he is obese, his lack of sensitivity to internal state will leave him without further motivation to eat, once he has finished the small meal. He will have eaten up all his cues, so to speak. Consider, on the other hand, the behavior we expect of an individual offered a very large meal. If he is not obese, he should leave some of it uneaten. If he is obese, he would be expected to eat most or all of the meal—in essence, he should eat until the cues are gone.

Subjects were invited to participate in an experiment involving the measurement of certain physiological variables. They were told that in order to obtain accurate base lines it was essential that they not eat after 9:00 A.M. on the day of participation. Appointments were made for early afternoon hours so that the minimum period of deprivation was 4 hours.

The experiment was run in conjunction with one of my unpublished studies that was not concerned with eating behavior. For the purposes of that study, bogus recording electrodes were attached to the subject and he performed a "monitoring" task for approximately 30 minutes. At the end of this period the experimenter announced that the experiment was over, disengaged the subject from his electrodes, and led him into another room "to fill out some final questionnaires."

Table 12.1. The number of sandwiches eaten as a function of the number offered and of weight. Numerals in parentheses are numbers of subjects; MS, mean square; F, Fisher statistic.

Weight of subject	No. of sandwiches eaten when offered	
	One	Three
Underweight	1.50(10)	1.62(10)
Normal	1.96(16)	1.88(12)
Overweight	1.48(9)	2.32(12)

Analysis of variance

Source	df	MS	F
Weight (W)	2	.90	3.48*
Number offered (N)	1	1.42	5.46*
W × N	2	1.29	4.97†
Error	63	.26	

* $P=.05$. † $P=.01$.

The new experimental room contained a refrigerator, a chair, and a table on which were a bottle of soda and either one roast beef sandwich or three roast beef sandwiches. Sandwiches were wrapped in white paper. While the subject sat down, the experimenter said casually: "Since you skipped lunch for the experiment, we'd like to give you lunch now. You can fill out the questionnaires while you eat. There are dozens more sandwiches in the refrigerator, by the way. Have as many as you want." The experimenter asked the subject to check by his office on the way out, and then left, shutting the door behind him.

Several aspects of the procedure were designed to reduce possible self-consciousness on the part of overweight subjects: (i) The experimenter was absent while the subject ate, and the meal was completely private. The subject could assume that he would not be interrupted because he was to go to the experimenter's office when he was through. (ii) The subject was told that there were dozens of sandwiches in the refrigerator and could assume that if he were to take a sandwich or two it would not be missed. (iii) The subject was given no reason to assume that the experimenter had the remotest interest in how many sandwiches he ate.

Male students, in Columbia University's summer school, 25 years old or younger, whose height and weight reports indicated that they were distinctly underweight, overweight, or of normal weight, were asked to participate in the experiment. The norms published by the Metropolitan Life Insurance Company (6) were used to establish percent weight deviation. The distribution of subjects' weight deviations was examined for those cutoff points that permitted a 5 percent weight differential between underweight and normal subjects and between normal and overweight subjects, and at the same time involved the minimum lost of subjects. The resulting range of weight deviations were -20 to -7 percent for underweight, -01 to $+09$ percent for normal, and $+15$ to $+48$ percent for overweight subjects.

This experiment, then, allows underweight, normal, and overweight subjects access to as much food as they care to eat. The only difference between experimental conditions is the number of sandwiches on the table in front of the subject. Overweight subjects responded powerfully to this difference (see Table 12.1). Those who were confronted with three sandwiches ate 57 percent more than those confronted with only one sandwich. In contrast, normal and underweight subjects were completely unaffected by the difference between experimental conditions—both groups ate as many sandwiches when they were initially offered one as when offered three.

A comparison of the absolute number of sandwiches eaten by the three weight groups in the two experimental conditions is striking. Overweight subjects ate markedly more than either normal or underweight subjects when they were confronted with three sandwiches (P for both groups, $<.05$). But when one sandwich was presented they ate as few as underweight subjects did and actually less than normal subjects ($P < .05$).

These findings suggest that the obese individual will habitually eat everything he is served in a typical meal. His susceptibility to external cues should compel him to clean his plate. Nonobese individuals, on the other hand, who eat primarily to reduce the discomfort of hunger, should frequently leave part of their meals uneaten.

In order to assess this implication subjects were asked, on the questionnaire after the experiment, "Are you a 'clean-your-plate' type or are you likely to leave something?" Alternatives were: "I nearly always clean my plate"; "I sometimes clean my plate and sometimes leave something"; or "I nearly always leave something." The same question was asked of a large sample of Yale undergraduates. Responses of the three weight groups were similar at the two schools and these responses are pooled in Table 12.2.

Table 12.2. Responses to the "clean-your-plate" question as a function of weight. N, number of subjects.

Weight of subject	N	Responses (%)		
		Nearly always clean my plate	Sometimes clean, sometimes leave	Nearly always leave something
Underweight	82	26.8	50.0	23.2
Normal	83	39.8	45.8	14.5
Overweight	95	53.7	36.8	9.5

The probability that an individual will habitually clean his plate is highly dependent on his weight. The X^2 based on Table 12.2 is 15.11, which for df = 4 is significant at the .005 level.

One aspect of the present experiment requires further discussion. It may have occurred to the reader that subjects offered one sandwich have a great many additional food cues. A refrigerator, filled with sandwiches, is across the room from them. Why then do overweight subjects not eat as many sandwiches when offered one as when offered three? (i) They may fail to do so because of the effort required to obtain food. Overweight subjects may simply have been unwilling to expend the necessary energy to cross the floor and get more sandwiches. It must be admitted that this explanation has an implausible ring, since the necessary effort was so slight. (ii) They may fail to do so because the additional food cues are not very salient or potent. Sandwiches on the table immediately in front of the subjects may compel eating; unseen sandwiches in a refrigerator may not. This alternative seems more plausible, especially in light of the present characterization of the obese. Strong, immediate food stimuli should be hard for the "external" individual to resist. Weaker, more distant stimuli may go unnoticed by the individual lacking internal motivation to seek out food.

Research on rats made obese by ventromedial hypothalamic lesions provides evidence that may be relevant to the results and interpretation of my study. In particular, an experiment by Miller *et al.* (7) on rats with these lesions parallels the present one to a remarkable degree. Their rats with lesions ate more palatable food that was freely available than control rats did, but when they were required to press a lever, run down an alley, or lift the heavy cover of a food cup to obtain their food, they ate less than the controls. These findings can be taken to mean that the hyperphagic rat is not only insensitive to satiety cues, since under normal circumstances it will overeat and grow fat, but insensitive to deprivation cues, since it appears to be unmotivated when there are obstacles to eating. This double insensitivity is, of course, precisely the characterization of obese humans that has been proposed by Schachter and his colleagues.

The experiment of Miller *et al.* is, moreover, open to the same interpretive possibilities as this study. Their animals with lesions may have eaten less in the "effortful" conditions because of the effort required to obtain food, or they may have eaten less in those conditions because the food stimuli were less potent. The various techniques they used to make the food more difficult to obtain would also have served to increase the distance from the food or otherwise reduce the potency of food cues.

The analogy between the hypothalamic obese rat and obese humans should be further explored, for other research has indicated parallels. Both the obese human (5, 8) and the hypothalamic obese rat (7, 9), for example, have been shown to be hyper-responsive to the taste properties of food.

References and notes

1. S. Schachter, in *Neurophysiology and Emotion*, D. Glass, Ed. (Rockefeller Univ. Press, New York, 1967), p. 117.
1a. A. Stunkard and C. Koch, *Arch. Gen. Psychiat.* **11**, 74 (1964).
2. S. Schachter, R. Goldman, A. Gordon, *J. Pers. Soc. Psychol.*, in press.
3. R. Goldman, M. Jaffa, S. Schachter, *ibid.*, in press.
4. S. Schachter and L. Gross, *ibid.*, in press.
5. R. Nisbett, *ibid.*, in press.
6. Metropolitan Life Insurance Company, *Statistical Bulletin* **40**, 2 (1941).

7. N. Miller, C. Bailey, J. Stevenson, *Science* **112**, 256 (1950).

8. S. Hashim and T. Van Itallie, *Ann. N.Y. Acad. Sci.* **131**, 654 (1965).

9. P. Teitelbaum, *J. Comp. Physiol. Psychol.* **48**, 156 (1955).

10. Supported in part by NSF grant S70373R. I am indebted to Sandor London, who suggested the study; to Harvey London, who made helpful comments on an early draft of the paper; and to Stanley Schachter, who contributed to every phase of the study. ◄

If you followed the four steps outlined for you before reading the article, you should be able to answer the following questions with little trouble. Do *not* refer back to the article.

Checking your involvement

1. This article is reprinted from _____ magazine.

2. T or F: The article makes good use of subheadings to divide the subject matter into major divisions or points.

3. The main idea of this article is that
   a. overweight subjects are more concerned with how food tastes than underweight subjects.
   b. overweight subjects nearly always clean their plates, as evidenced by Tables 12.1 and 12.2.
   c. overweight subjects are more susceptible to external food cues than underweight subjects.

4. The word *adulterated* as used in the article means
   a. illegitimate.
   b. to make inferior.
   c. characteristic of an adult.

5. Table 12.1 shows
   a. the number of sandwiches eaten by members of two groups.
   b. the number of sandwiches eaten by members of three groups.
   c. responses to "clean-your-plate" questionnaire.

6. T or F: If it is true that overweight individuals respond to external rather than internal cues, it should be possible to control the amount of food they eat by limiting the number of external cues that encourage eating.

7. In question 6 (above), the word *cues* refers to

   _____

   _____.

8. In the experiment described by the author,
   a. the subjects did not know the sandwiches were part of the experiment.
   b. the subjects did know the sandwiches were part of the experiment.

      c. the sandwiches were not intended to be part of the experiment,
but became a useful method of investigation.

  9. In the list of references and notes following the article, the name
which appears most often and the person the author thanks for contributing to the study is

    a. The Metropolitan Life Insurance Company.

    b. A. Stunkard.   c. S. Schachter.

 10. Combining the experiment described on humans and the experiments with rats, you can conclude that

_____

_____

_____.

If you followed through on all four steps, these questions should have been easy for you. Check your answers with these: 1. *Science*, 2. F, 3. c, 4. b, 5. b, 6. T, 7. internal cues are signs of hunger, such as gastric pains; external cues are foods in sight, 8. a, 9. c, 10. while further study is recommended, it would appear that an obese individual's eating might be controlled by allowing very few external cues.

Filling out reading reports on cards

Often you can't mark up an article as you did here, and often it isn't necessary. Some instructors don't ask for research papers, but do require reading reports based on outside reading (see Chapter 1). The basic reason for these reports is to familiarize you with some of the outside sources and to acquaint you with material not available in the textbook. These reading assignments are usually reported on 5 × 8 cards.

Here's an example of what a complete reading report card might contain:

Nisbett, Richard. "Determinants of Food Intake in Obesity," <u>Science</u>, Vol. 159, No. 3820 (March 15, 1968), pp. 1254-1255.

Experiments and questionnaires seem to indicate that obese individuals are more susceptible to external cues (food in sight) than non-obese individuals. Research on rats seems to substantiate this theory.

More can be found about obesity in Schachter, Neurophysiology & Emotion. Rockefeller Univ. Press, 1967.

Notice that the author's name, the article title, the source, the date, and page numbers appear in the order you would use in a bibliography. It is always a good idea to copy the information correctly and in that order in the event you need a bibliography or should ever use the card for a research paper. Notice, too, that the card contains a summary of the main points of the article plus a personal comment. How much you need to write or include beyond this is up to your individual instructor.

When you use library references, make sure you write down all the information you'll need. Check what you've written before you leave the library so that later you won't have to waste time looking up something you forgot to write down.

Doing the research paper

A research project and your outside reading assignments offer you a chance to compare your classroom knowledge with knowledge from other sources. The more sources you have the time and inclination to read, the broader and deeper your knowledge of a subject can be. Outside reading assignments let you know what people think about the issues you are studying. They help you relate what you have learned in the past to what you are learning now, and they open your eyes to problems and situations you never knew existed. You need them to make you look at your own beliefs and decide whether you have based your opinion on facts or on folly. A research project can be well worth the time.

Often the most difficult part of doing a term project is getting started. Once you've decided what you want to do, it's just a matter of doing it. Normally, however, you hear about the project at the beginning of the course, often on the first day. The instructor wants you to be involved with the course from the start, and he's right. On the other hand, some science projects can't be decided upon right away. If science is a fairly new or tough course for you, you may not know what type of project to do.

To get involved, first set up an appointment with your instructor so that you can either have him explain more fully what he wants or help you decide on a project for your paper. He can suggest some projects worth doing if you're short on ideas. After you and the instructor are satisfied with the proposed project, you're ready to go to work on it.

Naturally, you can use the methods already discussed in this chapter to help you find sources and take notes on them. Using the card catalogue, the *Readers' Guide*, roaming the 500 or *Q* section of the library as well as the science periodicals, and using the sources listed in this chapter are all means to finding sources for your subject.

After you have taken notes from sources, you will need to put them together into a paper. At this point, you must connect or synthesize your notes with what you have learned in your English classes about writing a reference paper. For detailed help in getting all your notes together for a paper, see either of the following:

James F. Lester. *Writing Research Papers.* Scott, Foresman and Company, 1967.

Kate L. Turabian. *Student's Guide for Writing College Papers.* University of Chicago Press, 1963.

SUMMARY

Here are five points to remember about reading outside sources:

1. Use outside reading as an extension of your textbook reading.
2. Use publications dealing specifically with your subject rather than sticking to the more familiar *Time-Life-Look* variety of magazines.
3. Use the four steps outlined in this chapter and take accurate notes. Keep track of the correct titles, volume numbers, and page numbers.
4. If you have a term project or research paper to do, don't wait until the last moment to do it.
5. Connect what you've learned in your English classes about writing papers with your science project.

The best place to practice using the library is obviously the library. If you want more practice in finding information, turn to pages 227–235 in the practices pages.

13

Taking Tests

The total picture. When you explore this chapter, you will find that it is divided into two parts. The first part shows you how to prepare for a test; the second, how to take a test. You'll find hints on how to take both objective and essay exams. As you read this chapter, look for what you *don't* know about taking tests. See how much of what you do know is presented here as well. If you have read one of the other books in this series (*How to Read the Social Sciences* or *How to Read the Humanities*), search out only the sections in this chapter that you haven't read before. Now explore the chapter.

Preparing for tests

It's past midnight and you'd like to be in bed, but you have to study. You've had a lot of coffee to help you stay awake, but it doesn't seem to help. The words blur and your mind wanders. You are cramming for a test, and it's a bad feeling. But what else can you do?

Cramming often seems to be the only way to prepare for a test. And it may have paid off for you before. On the other hand, where does it all lead? Some of the information you stuff into your head tonight may still be with you tomorrow. But you'll start to forget most of it right after the test. When you take final exams later on, you'll probably have to go through the same thing all over again. And what about five years from now? How much of your knowledge will stay with you if it was all merely crammed?

Psychologists say that a majority of people forget about 80 percent of what they learn in school. Surely one reason for this great waste of knowledge is the common habit of reading and studying just to pass tests.

Ideally, tests should be a means, not an end. They should be an opportunity for you to solidify your knowledge, not a threat forcing you to absorb great quantities of information under pressure. Of course, things are seldom as they should be, and you are a rare student if you never feel pressured by an upcoming test. Nevertheless, you can learn to deal with tests in a way that turns them into an opportunity for learning.

You know the first rule: do your work day by day. Most teachers suggest that you spend two hours studying for every hour spent in class. If you have 15 hours of classes, this means 30 hours of study—a 45-hour week. (Successful studying is a full-time job.) If you apply the four steps for reading to your other subjects, you will find that this amount of time is needed.

But beyond your daily study habits, there are some specific things you can do to prepare for tests more efficiently. Here is a list that should remind you of the best ways to get ready for an examination.

Before the Test: A Checklist

1. If your instructor gives objective tests (multiple choice, true-false, completion), try to think of questions he might ask. Skim and review your notes, either in the book or in your notebook, and frame possible questions in your mind.

2. Try writing a brief summary or commentary for each chapter you have studied. This will force you to put into your own words the knowledge you gain from Step Three: *Analyze for Comprehension.*

3. Recite to yourself the important names, theories, dates, terms—any relevant information connected with what you have been studying in class.

4. Take the time to define the key words in each chapter. Words such as *mitosis, ecology, chromosomes* may be familiar to you, but could you explain them in your own words for a test?

5. Put together what you've learned from lectures, class reading, and outside reading.

6. Look over the last test you took to figure out the type of questions you can expect and to recall the instructor's comments on that test.

Taking tests

"Whatever you do, don't get panicky over a test!" How many times have you heard that advice? There should be no cause for panic if you've studied properly in advance of the test. But tests can be unnerving, and you may lower your score significantly by failing to observe some common-sense rules. To help prevent that, study the following rules now but review them before your next test so that they will be second nature to you when the pressure is on.

Things to Do During the Test

1. Read the test directions carefully *before* you begin to mark any answers. If the directions are not clear, ask the instructor to clarify them for you before you start. Don't try to guess what they mean.

2. Make certain that you understand the grading system. If some questions are worth more than others, give them more time and effort.

3. Keep track of the time. When you begin the test, try to decide how much time you'll need to answer each question, and budget your time accordingly.

4. Explore all the questions, then begin with the ones you can answer most readily. Answering what you are sure of first will help you bring out all that you know and remember.

5. Make certain that you *answer* the questions. Don't get so carried away that you write irrelevant answers.

6. Try to save some time at the end of the testing period to go over your test, filling in possible blanks, and proofreading your written answers.

7. Write legibly. Remember, the instructor doesn't have time to decipher scribbles.

Read before you leap

Of the rules listed above, by far the most important is the first: read the directions carefully *before* you begin to mark any answers. Here is a sample test that illustrates this point. Try it.

> This is a test to determine how well you are able to follow directions. Accuracy is more important than speed; you will have all the time you need to complete the test. Before beginning, read the test through once carefully to make sure you understand all the directions.

1. Circle every word in the directions above which begins with the letter *a*.
2. Underline two nouns in the above directions.
3. Count and write down the number of three-letter words in directions 2, 5, and 6.
4. Cross out all commas in the first two lines of the directions paragraph.
5. Fill in the centers of all the *o*'s in the third line of the first paragraph of this test.
6. Do not follow any of the first five numbered directions. Do not make any mark on this test.

This put-on test often fools students. Even though they are warned to read the entire set of directions before doing anything, they start out with number 1 and work right up to 6 without carefully reading the directions first. You might remember this test the next time you take a real one.

Taking subjective or essay tests

Tests in the sciences sometimes include essay questions. Some questions may require very long answers, some shorter ones. Short-answer questions can be tricky, especially those so worded that you are left in doubt about the kind of answer expected. For example, take the following question from a Biology 1 test:

1. What is the process called *mitosis*?

Before you can answer a question like this, you need to know whether the instructor wants an answer like this:

> *Mitosis* is the term given to a common method of cell division (sometimes called equational division) in which the nuclear chromation is formed into a long thread which in turns breaks into chromosomes that are split lengthwise. The halves then come together in two sets, each forming the nucleus for a new cell.

or like this:

> *Mitosis* is the process by which a cell divides to form another cell. Mitosis includes several stages of division going from interphase through stages called prophase, metaphase, anaphase, telophase, and back to interphase, where one cell would then be two.

Notice that both these answers discuss the process called mitosis. The first is more of a dictionary or glossary definition. The second also tells what mitosis is but it names the stages rather than explaining them. Which answer would earn the most points depends upon what the instructor wants you to answer. You can determine this by the amount of space given for an answer, by the number of points the question is worth, by experience with previous tests given by this instructor, or by asking him how detailed an answer he wants.

The question itself is somewhat vague and invites a vague answer, but a good response will still give specific information. It is always risky to give information not asked for, and in this case you need to know what the instructor wants.

Answering long essay questions that are worth many points requires more sophisticated skills. In a long answer, you will include a great deal of information and most of it should be specific, not general, information. You will need to be precise and make sure that everything you say is relevant to the question. For this you need two main abilities: to be able to detect the key words in the question, and to know how to organize your ideas.

Here are some key direction-words used in essay exams. See if you can write a definition for each word. Then compare your answers with the definitions that follow.

1. compare
2. contrast
3. define
4. describe
5. discuss
6. enumerate
7. evaluate
8. explain
9. interpret
10. prove or show

Here are answers to compare with yours.

1. *compare:* show the similarities between two events, periods, ideas, theories, or the like. (Some people use *compare* to mean showing differences as well as similarities, so be careful.)

2. *contrast:* show the differences between two or more events, periods, ideas, theories, or the like.

3. *define:* state the meaning of a word or phrase. Example: Define *science.*

4. *describe:* give the characteristics of something. Example: Describe the functions of the ATP/ADP systems.

5. *discuss:* give the pros and cons on an issue, event, process, theory, or technique. Example: Discuss how DNA replicates itself.

6. *enumerate:* list a number of reasons or attributes of something. Example: Enumerate the stages of mitosis.

7. *evaluate:* make a judgment or give an opinion, or supply reasons why something is as it is. Example: Evaluate the effects of Jenner's experiments with cowpox.

8. *explain:* support or qualify a given generalization with specific facts and ideas. Example: Explain what is meant by the "scientific method."

9. *interpret:* analyze critically or explain something not clear. Example: Interpret Table 12.2 in the article on obesity (page 143).

10. *prove* or *show:* demonstrate the truth of a statement, explain the reasons for events turning out as they did, or speculate on what might be the effects of certain causes. Example: Show with diagrams how the eye is like a camera.

An understanding of these words will permit you to control what you say. To write an effective essay you must apply your knowledge to the question and stick to the point. It isn't enough just to write down everything you know.

Try your hand at writing an answer in the space below to the following question about this book.

Enumerate and explain the ways to develop your vocabulary mentioned in Step Two of this book.

Your answer can be stated in several ways. But it should enumerate or list (1) key roots and affixes; (2) personalized vocabulary cards; (3) books on vocabulary building. In addition, each one of these three methods should be explained so that you show an understanding of how the method works. For example:

One method of developing vocabulary is to make vocabulary

cards for the words you want to learn. Print the word you wish to learn on one side of a card and on the other side the definition, a synonym, and a sentence with the word used in context. Keep these word cards in a stack and spend a few minutes each day reviewing the words quickly to see if you can pronounce the word and recall the meaning without looking at the back of the card. The idea is to learn the words by going over and over them daily until they are familiar.

Each one of the three methods should be explained in a similar way. Notice that the basic elements are the name of the method, an explanation of the method, and the purpose for the method.

Before your next test, review this section of the book. Reviewing will help you remember some basic tips on test-taking which could mean the difference between passing and failing.

Taking objective tests

If you have problems expressing yourself in written essay tests, you probably prefer objective tests because you don't have to organize what you know into a formal, written answer. Objective tests are often easier because they usually require only literal comprehension, not critical or affective comprehension. Sometimes, if you don't know an answer, you can eliminate items until you have a pretty good idea what the correct response is. And if that doesn't work, you can always guess.

On the other hand, when you take objective tests you usually need a wealth of such data as facts, names, definitions, causes, and effects to be able to supply the right response.

The following are some pointers on taking different types of objective tests.

Multiple-choice tests

1. Do all the questions you know first, checking or circling the numbers of the ones you want to come back to later.
2. Read all the possible answers before selecting one. For example, molecular movement
   a. is random.
   b. is frictionless.
   c. is constant.
   d. is all of these.
   On quick reading, you might feel *a* or *b* is the correct answer, mark it, and move on, but a careful look would show that *d* is the answer.
3. Use the process of elimination discounting the answers you know are wrong. For example: A scientific theory: (a) is an educated guess;

(b) has predictive value; (c) is truth discovered after long investigation; (d) none of these. By elimination *b* is probably the best answer. Can you see why? What is a *theory?*

4. Watch out for questions that begin, "Which one is not an example of . . . ." For example: Which one is not a stage of meiosis? If you skip over the word *not,* you might pick out a stage you recognize as meiosis and mark it without seeing that many other stages are also listed.

5. Make certain that you mark the answers according to the directions, not the way you presume they should be marked.

True-False tests

1. For a statement to be marked true, the entire statement must be true. But for a statement to be marked false, only one part need be false.

2. Find out whether you will lose points if you guess. Some instructors consider wrong only those answers that you actually mark incorrectly; others consider every unanswered question wrong.

3. Mark your answer sheet the way the directions tell you to mark it. Just because it is a true-false test doesn't necessarily mean you use *T* and *F.*

4. Read each question carefully, looking for words that tend to make statements false. The following words don't always make a statement false, but they should alert you to think carefully.

   all: A good reader should be able to read *all* materials at the same speed.

   always: Great scientists are *always* great experimenters.

   never: The glucose molecules can *never* be joined together by hydrolysis.

   none: *None* of the characteristics of science ever change.

   only: *Only* scientists and their objective views can solve man's problems.

5. Read each question carefully, looking for qualifying words that tend to make statements true, such as the following:

   some: *Some* readers may be able to read at 2000 words per minute, but most readers can't.

   sometimes: *Sometimes* a hydrogen atom has more than one electron; it is then called heavy hydrogen.

   usually: Glass is *usually* an insulator.

   most: *Most* scientists work in laboratories.

Here's a word of caution, however. Instructors are aware of the power of these words, too. The only real way to be certain that the words are being used correctly is to know the answer to the question.

Matching tests

1. Read the directions carefully. Look at the following examples and notice the difference in directions.
    a. Match the items in Column I with those in Column II. You may use the items in Column I more than once.
    b. Match the items in Column I with those in Column II. You may not use the items in Column II more than once.
2. As you match each item, mark off the ones that you use *if* you are not allowed to use them twice.
3. Match the ones you are sure of first. Then go through the process of eliminating the ones you think might belong together.
4. Don't waste time figuring out questions whose answers you don't know until you have answered all the ones you are certain you do know.

SUMMARY

When you walk into an exam with pen in hand, there's no substitute for knowing the material on which you're being tested. This book can help you understand what you've read for a test, but this chapter doesn't show you how to pass an exam. It does show you the mechanics of taking tests. These practical hints can keep you from failing on a test.

Practice Step Four: *Synthesize for Understanding.* Use all four steps together by doing the exercises on pages 237–247 in the practices section.

14

Making Personal Connections

The total picture. In this final chapter, you are urged to reflect on what you read by becoming personally involved. A good reader tries to understand what his reading means to him personally, even though his attitude toward the material may be negative. Unfortunately, there is no easy set of rules for accomplishing total reading involvement. It is hoped that the previous chapters have helped you become more involved to some extent. But no one can tell you what reading a book has to do with your life. Maybe this chapter can help you make the connection between your own life and what you read in science.

Personal connections

It's doubtful that you could get through a day without coming into contact with science. From the food you eat and the clothes you wear to the way you think, science is part of your life. Stop for a moment and think what your life would be like without science. Try to think of all the things in your life necessary for a comfortable living that are not connected with science.

The number of things you were able to think of depends on the kind of life you lead. Certainly there would be no phonograph records, no television, no radio, no newspapers, no books, no telephones, no cars, no houses as we know them, no gas or electric furnaces or stoves, no drug stores, no frozen foods, no safe milk, butter, cheeses, or meats, no glasses to correct your vision, and so on.

Of course, you might say that there would also be no nuclear weapons, no napalm bombs, no B-52's, no tanks, no flamethrowers, and so on. This is a question of conscience that scientists have struggled with for years. How we use the products of modern science is, of course, the concern of everyone.

Many of the things mentioned in the two previous paragraphs connect you with science, some more personally than others. But when you go to your science class or when you try to read your science assignments, how personally involved are you? It isn't always easy to adjust your everyday personal life and interests to the problems of getting through a science class.

In the previous paragraphs we have intentionally stressed the applications of science. This is only part of the story—the most obvious part. Science is concerned more with ideas than with technology, and these ideas help us to understand the natural world better. Science influences the way you think, and it influences the way you perceive everything from the stars in the sky to the cold in your head. Science is finding out, and if the scientist finds things out because he's curious, so can you.

The whole aim of this book is to help you read better in the sciences. You've been shown mechanical methods for exploring, for vocabulary development, for analysis, and for retaining what you read. But one thing you can't be shown is how to change your attitude if it is a hindrance to good reading.

Attitudes can and do change. The more you live and experience things, the more you have to connect personal experiences with what you read. Your "connecting" may be like Walt Whitman's when he wrote:

When I Heard the Learn'd Astronomer

Walt Whitman

When I heard the learn'd astronomer,
When the proofs, the figures, were ranged in columns before
    me,
When I was shown the charts and diagrams, to add, divide, and
    measure them,
When I sitting heard the astronomer where he lectured with much
    applause in the lecture-room,
How soon unaccountable I became tired and sick,
Till rising and gliding out I wander'd off by myself,
In the mystical moist night-air, and from time to time,
Look'd up in perfect silence at the stars.

Or science may suddenly become important to you as you accept or reject ideas in books such as Rachel Carson's *Silent Spring*, in which she attacks the reckless use of chemicals that are poisoning the earth.

►   The current vogue for poisons has failed utterly to take into account these most fundamental considerations. As crude a weapon as the cave man's club, the chemical barrage has been hurled against the fabric of life—a fabric on the one hand delicate and destructible, on the other miraculously tough and resilient, and capable of striking back in unexpected ways. These extraordinary capacities of life have been ignored by the practitioners of chemical control who have brought to their task no "high-minded orientation," no humility before the vast forces with which they tamper.

The "control of nature" is a phrase conceived in arrogance, born of the Neanderthal age of biology and philosophy, when it was supposed that nature exists for the convenience of man. The concepts and practices of applied entomology for the most part date from that Stone Age of science. It is our alarming misfortune that so primitive a science has armed itself with the most modern and terrible weapons, and that in turning them against the insects it has also turned them against the earth.[1] ◄

Or perhaps an interest in the sea and skin diving might lead you to books such as *The Silent World* by Jacques Cousteau, one of the world's most knowledgeable men on the subject, with such challenges as this:

►   Obviously man has to enter the sea. There is no choice in the matter. The human population is increasing so rapidly and land resources are being depleted at such a rate, that we must take sustenance from the great cornucopia. The flesh and vegetables of the sea are vital. The necessity for taking mineral and chemical resources from the sea is plainly indicated by the intense political and economic struggles over tidal oil fields and the "continental shelf," by no means confined to Texas and California.

Our best independent diving range is only halfway down to the border of the shelf. We are not yet able to occupy the ground claimed by the statesmen. When research centers and industrialists apply themselves to the problem we will advance to the six-hundred-foot "dropoff" line. It will require much better equipment than the aqualung. The lung is primitive and unworthy of contemporary levels of science. We believe, however, that the conquerors of the shelf will have to get wet.[2] ◄

Or your attitude may change with a sudden desire to know what $E = mc^2$ really means.

Or your attitude may never change.

---

[1] From *Silent Spring* by Rachel Carson. Copyright © 1962 by Rachel L. Carson. Reprinted by permission of Houghton Mifflin Company.

[2] From *The Silent World* by J. Y. Cousteau and Frederic Dumas. Copyright 1953 by Harper & Brothers. Reprinted by permission of Harper & Row, Publishers.

Naturally, you can't live everything and see everything. That's where reading can come in. Reading enables you to share the experiences of others. And that, along with your own experience, is what education is all about.

Unfortunately, our educational system sometimes does not seem to encourage connecting what you read. When you go to class, you generally take up each subject separately — an hour of chemistry, an hour of psychology, and an hour of English. You may begin to feel as if all these things are separate and unconnected. But as a student, you can learn to connect them.

Assuming that you don't want to waste the thirteen chapters you've read so far, the following article from a science journal is reproduced for you to read. But don't just read it. Explore it, check the vocabulary, analyze for good comprehension, mark it as you read, and then connect it with what you already know about the subject. In other words, use all four steps. And do it with the proper attitude.

► ## Carbon Monoxide and Air Pollution from Automobile Emissions in New York City[3]

Kenneth L. Johnson, L. H. Dworetzky,
and Austin N. Heller

ABSTRACT. *Local business-day traffic determines the diurnal carbon monoxide concentrations at individual sites in Manhattan. Concentrations during the day can be predicted from readings taken in early morning.*

The Department of Air Pollution Control of the City of New York has embarked upon an intensive program to control carbon monoxide. The program is based upon the measurement of carbon monoxide emissions and the behavior of the gas in the atmosphere at different locations under different conditions. The Department estimated the daily emissions of pollutants from automobiles for each square mile in the city. Estimated totals of these emissions for the entire city were:

Carbon monoxide	4140 ton/day
Hydrocarbons	560 ton/day
Oxides of nitrogen	106 ton/day

The estimates indicated that midtown and lower Manhattan were

---

[3]From *Science*, Vol. 160, No. 3823 (April 5, 1968), 67–68. Copyright 1968 by the American Association for the Advancement of Science.

main sources of automobile exhaust gases. Steps were taken to determine how local traffic conditions influence the atmospheric concentrations of automobile exhaust gases measured at a given location.

Equipment to monitor continually carbon monoxide concentrations was installed near street level at five locations in Manhattan. The largest amount of valid data was obtained at 110 East 45 Street from 6 January through 17 May 1967, and from 30 July through 14 September. The sampling probe was set approximately 15 feet above the pavement and 5 feet into the street from the curb. A continuous flow of air was analyzed and recorded 24 hours per day, 7 days per week. The average hourly concentrations exceeded 15 parts per million from 9:00 a.m. to 7:00 p.m. New York State recommended that carbon monoxide concentrations of 15 parts per million for 8 consecutive hours should not be exceeded more than 15 percent of the time.

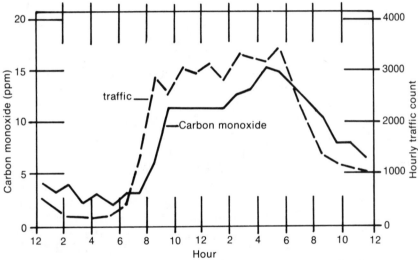

Figure 14.1. Hourly average carbon monoxide concentration of and traffic count at East 45 Street; *ppm*, parts per million.

The apparent correlation between the business day and measured atmospheric carbon monoxide concentrations spurred further investigation, the results of which are shown in Figure 14.1. They show simultaneous hourly traffic counts and hourly average concentrations of carbon monoxide for 4 April 1967. The traffic volumes for each hour are the totals for all traffic moving on Park Avenue past 45th Street itself. The shapes of the curves for traffic count and carbon monoxide are markedly similar, indicating that local concentrations of atmospheric carbon monoxide are strongly influenced by local traffic conditions.

The data obtained from the carbon monoxide samplers operated during portions of 1967 indicate that: (i) Business-day traffic determines the basic shape of the curve for diurnal carbon monoxide concentration in Manhattan. (ii) Local traffic conditions are the primary influence upon concentrations of carbon monoxide measured close to street level. The problem of automobile exhaust for a large city or metropolitan area may be the sum of local problems related to local traffic conditions.

An effort is being made to predict the hourly average concentrations of carbon monoxide for each day. When the average concentration of carbon monoxide is plotted against the time of day, the resulting curves are similar in shape from station to station, although their amplitudes and time phases differ. Therefore, we attempted to predict hourly concentrations of carbon monoxide from readings taken in the very early morning. Accordingly, the curves were smoothed through the use of a 2-hour moving average. Each of the smoothed hourly values was then divided by the midnight average, C_0. To predict the hourly concentrations of carbon monoxide, we first determined C_0 by direct measurement. We then forecast the concentration at each hour of the following day by multiplying C_0 by the ratio indicated on the average curve for that station. When this method was used to predict daily peaks, the predicted values fell within 5 parts per million of the measured values about 70 percent of the time for stations at Park Avenue South, Times Square, Herald Square, and East 45 Street.

The limitations of this predictive method are dictated by the dispersion in the hourly averaged data. The mean daily standard deviation is between 4 and 5 parts per million. This is consistent with the error in the predictions. There is a cause-and-effect relationship between traffic and carbon monoxide concentration. Hourly averages of traffic volume for the five sites were obtained from the Traffic Department. These data were smoothed and normalized in exactly the same fashion as the carbon monoxide data were. In order to eliminate time between the two sets of data, the relative carbon monoxide concentration, C/C_0, was plotted against T/T_0. In Figure 14.2, a curve has been drawn through the points in the chronological order in which they appear.

Carbon monoxide concentration and traffic volume are periodic functions of time, and each can be represented by a Fourier series. When time is eliminated between the two functions and they are plotted as orthogonal coordinates (Figure 14-2), closed curves somewhat akin to Lissajous figures should result.

The carbon monoxide concentration and the traffic volume are not in phase, and accordingly the increases and decreases in the curves do not coincide. The carbon monoxide concentration lags the

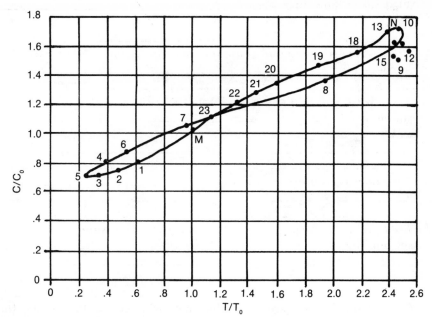

Figure 14.2. Normalized concentration – traffic curve at East 45 Street.

traffic volume during the increase and much of the decrease in the curve. Carbon monoxide concentration does not build up as rapidly as the traffic perhaps because the traffic exhausts into a relatively clean atmosphere in which dilution is relatively good. A relatively dirty atmosphere prevents the carbon monoxide concentration of the traffic from decreasing as rapidly as the traffic does. This phase shift is consistent with a diffusion process.

For all sites the carbon monoxide concentration and the traffic volume are nearly in phase from midnight until some hour between 3 and 5 a.m. Thus, the decay rate of the carbon monoxide increases after the concentration and traffic volumes fall below a certain value characteristic of each station. This phenomenon may explain the crossing of traffic volume and carbon monoxide curves as each begins to increase and again when they fall off. ◄

To prove to yourself that you did a good job on all four steps, answer the following questions without referring back to the article. All of the questions require short answers.

1. State the main idea of the article in one sentence. _____
_____

2. Who conducted the experiment? _____
_____

3. What does Figure 14.1 reveal? _____

_____

4. What is the estimated daily emission of carbon monoxide for the entire city per day? _____

_____

5. What two theories did the data obtained from the carbon monoxide samplers indicate? _____

_____

_____

6. What does C_0 represent in Figure 14.2? _____

_____

7. What probable reason is given for the carbon monoxide concentration not building up as rapidly as the traffic does? _____

_____

_____

8. At what time of day are the carbon monoxide concentration and the traffic volume nearly in phase? _____

_____

9. What is the basic writing pattern of this article? _____

10. What effects can this study and others like it have on you personally?

_____

_____

Compare your answers with the following. There will be some difference in wording, but the basic ideas should be the same.

1. Local business-day traffic determines the diurnal carbon monoxide concentration at individual sites in Manhattan. (See "Abstract" statement at the opening of the article.)

2. The Department of Air Pollution Control of the City of New York. (See the opening sentence of the article.)

3. Hourly average carbon monoxide concentration at traffic count at one Manhattan site. (See caption under Figure 14.1.)

4. 4140 tons per day. (See first paragraph.)

5. (1) Business-day traffic determines the basic shape of the curve for carbon monoxide concentration in Manhattan. (2) Local traffic conditions are the primary influence upon concentrations of carbon monoxide. (See fourth paragraph.)

6. The midnight average of carbon monoxide. (See fifth paragraph.)

7. Because the traffic exhausts into a relatively clean atmosphere. (See second from last paragraph.)

8. From midnight until some hour between 3 and 5 a.m. (See second from last paragraph.)

9. The overall pattern is one of problem-solving. (The pattern is there because a problem is stated, and the attempt to solve the problem through investigation and experimentation is presented.)

10. Answers will vary. But air pollution in cities is an ever growing concern for all plant and animal life.

The New York air-pollution problem may not be of much concern to you. Then neither may cell division, atom particles, soil erosion, and many other matters you will encounter in your science classes. But to get good comprehension when reading about any of these topics, you must approach them with an attitude of willingness. You must look for some connection between the article and you.

For instance, the article you just read can concern you, even if you don't live in New York City. Every city is concerned with the air-pollution problem. You may not be worried about it right now because you can still breathe and still see the stars at night. But as each year goes by the problem gets worse. What does polluted air do to your lungs? Will it cut down your life expectancy? How much worse can we expect it to get? Can smog-control devices on cars really help? How much will these devices cost if a law is passed making control devices mandatory? How much of your tax money is spent on air-pollution study? Questions such as these can help you "connect" with what you read. A good general question to ask yourself when you read an article or textbook chapter is "How does this affect me?"

Some connections are easier to make than others just because of natural interests. But ask yourself—why are you going to college? What do you want to learn and why? How well do you want to learn? Just remember that those things you can connect to your own life will stay with you longer. The last step in reading to learn is to make your reading meaningful not for a teacher or a test, but for you as a human being. It's the most important step—and the most enjoyable.

SUMMARY

Up to now you've been learning to read. This last step is reading to learn. It's putting all four steps together into one total reading process. This chapter emphasized that to get the most from your reading, you have to relate what you read to your own life.

There are no exercises on connecting in the practice pages. To get the most from this book now, skim over each step again and try to connect each part with your reading problems. You haven't finished learning how to read the sciences just because you've finished this book. In fact, you're really just starting. Now you should connect this book with whatever you have to read in the sciences.

Practices in Reading the Sciences

The following pages give you a chance to practice what you have learned about reading the sciences. The first section provides practice in Step One: *Explore*. You'll find selections from science textbooks, magazines, anthologies, and laboratory manuals. All of them are to be used for practice in exploring. The second section provides practice in Step Two: *Check the Vocabulary*. Exercises deal with words in context, word roots and affixes, dictionary usage, and rapid word recognition in the sciences. The third section provides practice in Step Three: *Analyze for Comprehension*. Here you will use some of the material from the first section for greater comprehension as well as some shorter selections from various science textbooks. The final section provides a complete chapter to which you can apply Step Four: *Synthesize for Understanding*.

The practice pages should help you develop the skills taught in this book. Don't worry if you make mistakes, but do try to understand why you made them. Reread questions you miss to figure out why the response in the answer key is better than yours. (For some questions, of course, there is no "right" answer.) If you can learn from your errors here, you can save yourself from making the same mistake in your actual class reading assignments and tests.

If you want to get the greatest benefit from what you have read in these pages, don't stop with the practices. Try to apply each idea to tomorrow's lesson in your science textbook and lab manual.

ONE

Explore

PRACTICE **1**

Directions. Explore the following Table of Contents from a science text-book. Look for the points mentioned in Chapter 1. Then answer the questions following the Table of Contents to check your skill at exploring.

CONTENTS[1]

Introduction

PART I

General Biological Background

PART II

The Fossil Record

[1]Reprinted with permission of The Macmillan Company from *Man's Evolution: An Introduction to Physical Anthropology* by C. Loring Brace and M. F. Ashley Montagu. © copyright, C. Loring Brace and M. F. Ashley Montagu, 1965.

See how well you can answer the following questions without looking back at the Table of Contents. Check your answers on p. 249.

1. The book is divided into _____ parts.
2. T or F: There is a glossary of terms in the book.
3. T or F: There is an index in the book.
4. According to the way the chapters are divided, the major emphasis will be placed on Part Two, _____.
5. This Table of Contents is probably for a book dealing primarily with
   a. chemistry.
   b. biology.
   c. anthropology.
   d. geology.

PRACTICE **2**

Directions. Explore the following Preface from a science textbook as you were shown in Chapter 1. Then answer the questions which follow the Preface without looking back for the answers. Check your answers on p. 249.

► Preface[2]

To prepare a book that represents contemporary psychology without becoming encyclopedic requires the exercise of considerable arbitrary judgment in the selection of material. While this edition, like the earlier ones, is abundantly documented (with some 1,200 citations of books and journal articles), such a selection merely scratches the surface of the literature, the magnitude of which can be estimated from the appearance of 16,000 new titles in a single year's *Psychological Abstracts*.

In deciding what to report from this massive production of scholarly materials we have been guided mainly by three criteria: *First*, we wish to represent fairly the residue from psychology's history, so that we do not discard classical studies merely because they are old. *Second*, we wish to represent the changing front of modern psychology; thus we do not include older topics merely because they conventionally have been included in textbooks. *Third*, we wish to acquaint students with the frontiers of contemporary psychology (for example, information-processing with the aid of modern high-speed computers); so fast has psychology been growing that over 40 percent of the citations in this edition, five years after the last edition, are new to it.

We might list as a *fourth* criterion in the choice of material our desire to meet the concerns of that large fraction of the students in our colleges and universities who find themselves, for various reasons, taking a first course in psychology. We know these students well through our association with them both inside and outside of class. They are not motivated primarily by the desire to learn the stock and trade of psychologists: instead they want to know what is relevant to their own lives, and to find answers to the questions raised by their own interests. To satisfy student interests is compatible with the scientific aspects of psychology; a course that arouses student

---

[2]From *Introduction to Psychology* by Ernest R. Hilgard and Richard C. Atkinson. Copyright 1953, © 1957, 1962, 1967 by Harcourt, Brace & World, Inc.

interest can fulfill the twin goals of being both pertinent and scholarly. The potential relevance of basic psychology to human problems can be shown; it is this eventual relevance that justifies the investment society makes in scientific endeavors. For example, one of our new chapters—Chapter 10, entitled "States of Awareness"—represents the renewed attention of contemporary psychologists to cognitive processes, and at the same time provides some answers to the student who is faced by a variety of claims on subjects ranging from consciousness-expanding drugs to sleep-learning courses. Our emphasis on developmental psychology—including adolescence and early adulthood—goes beyond that in most beginning textbooks because we know that the student is trying to find and define his own identity in this period between recent adolescence and the adult world.

Among topics that reflect the current areas of excitement among psychologists we may select a few to give something of the flavor of new emphases in this edition: the problem of critical periods versus stages in development; the distinction within theories of identification between sex-role and non-sex-role identification; local versus central determiners of hunger and thirst; distinctively human motivation according to three viewpoints (behavior theory, the theory of unconscious determination, and cognitive theory that includes the approaches of humanistic psychology); threshold psychophysics versus detection theory; sleep, dreams, drugs, and hypnosis; information-processing models of learning, including computer-based instruction; new developments in neurophysiological and related theories of memory, including the topics of short-term memory and the "tip-of-the-tongue" phenomenon; adjustive coping mechanisms recognized alongside defense mechanisms; expanded treatment of behavior disorders and psychotherapy, with attention to the behavior therapies.

The newer materials to which reference has just been made are but a few specimens of topics that have been integrated within a book that follows essentially its old outline—an outline that has been based in no small part on the replies to questionnaires submitted by teachers who have used the earlier editions. It is clear from these questionnaires that no one chapter order will please all instructors; some have in the past preferred to select certain chapters, omitting others, and to teach these selected chapters in an order according to individual choice. Instructors report that this works out satisfactorily so long as they provide a few transitions to chapters that are assigned in novel order.

For those who teach shorter courses, we recommend selecting a few chapters and treating them more fully. The obligation to "cover the ground" should never be allowed to interfere with a better coverage of those topics that are carefully considered. Additional suggestions on instruction are included in the accompanying *Instructor's Manual*.

Critical discussions have been included again because they provide an opportunity for examining areas of uncertainty and conflict within psychology without unduly cluttering the free flow of the text. Some instructors may prefer to omit these, others to expand upon them. References at the ends of chapters often contain more material of an advanced nature than it would be feasible to assign. They are there as aids to the reader who may wish to delve further into a topic. If the course calls for one or more term papers, these lists are valuable as aids to scholarship of greater depth on a specified topic. ◄

1. This preface was written for the _____ edition of the book.
   a. first   c. third
   b. second   d. fourth
2. Developmental psychology, including adolescence and early adulthood, is emphasized because
   a. students are trying to find and define their own identity.
   b. it represents the changing front of psychology.
   c. it acquaints students with psychology.
3. T or F: According to the author, there have been fewer than 10,000 new titles to select from as reported in *Psychological Abstracts*.
4. T or F: The present edition, for which this preface was written, is similar to the last edition except for a few indicated changes.
5. Which of the following issues have been incorporated into this edition of the book?
   a. problems of critical periods versus stages in development
   b. sleep, dreams, drugs, and hypnosis
   c. treatment of behavior disorders
   d. all of the above
6. T or F: Critical discussions have been included because they provide an opportunity for examining areas of uncertainty and conflict within psychology.

Stokes, Wm. _Essentials of Earth History_, p. 199
Ch. 11 "The Ordovician Period" Classification
and definition of some common Ordovician
animals

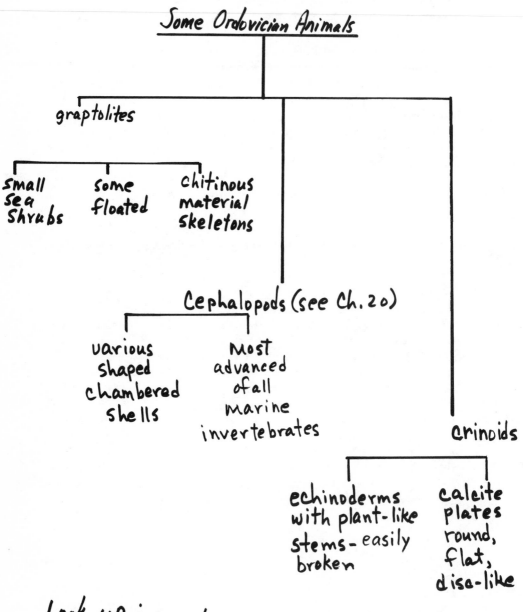

Some Ordovician Animals

graptolites

- small sea shrubs
- some floated
- chitinous material skeletons

Cephalopods (see Ch. 20)

- various shaped chambered shells
- Most advanced of all marine invertebrates

crinoids

- echinoderms with plant-like stems - easily broken
- calcite plates round, flat, disc-like

Look up: echinoderm
calcite

172

PRACTICE **3**

Directions. Explore the following chapter from a psychology textbook. Follow the directions you were given in Chapter 2. (See p. 13.) Then answer the questions that follow the sample chapter selection. Check your answers on p. 249.

► ## Ability to Learn and Remember[3]

If we are to manage our learning experiences successfully, it is important that we know as much as we can about our ability to learn and remember, about the possibility of increasing it through our own efforts, and about what changes in it we can expect as we grow older.

Is there an "all-round" ability to learn and remember?

In an age of rapidly changing technology, which demands the acquisition of new knowledge and skill as a measure to prevent unemployment, it is clearly important to know whether or not learning ability is specific to particular kinds of tasks or situations. Until recently, most available evidence had not indicated a general learning factor. If there were such a thing, we would expect to find high intercorrelations among performance scores on different kinds of learning tasks. But most studies have found such intercorrelations to be low (Husband, 1939). Nor has the technique of factor analysis indicated any general learning capacity (Woodrow, 1940; Heese, 1942).

Failure to find evidence of general learning capacity in these studies may result from the way the experiments are usually designed. The conventional measure of gain from learning is defined as the difference in performance between the beginning and end of practice. But such a definition of gain is almost certain to give an incorrect measure of learning capacity, since the original measures reflect *both* capacity and whatever prior unrecorded experience the subject may have had with such tasks. The higher his capacity and the greater his previous practice, the better the subject's initial performance will be and the less room he will have for further learning. Thus a subject with *less* learning capacity might even show *more* learning during the practice session, simply because there is more left for him to learn. It follows, then, that a factor analysis based on

---

[3]Ruch, *op. cit.*, pp. 243–248.

such data probably would not reveal a general learning factor, even if such a factor did exist. By the use of statistical methods of greater sophistication which control for this discrepancy in initial status, some evidence of a general ability has been obtained (Ruch, 1936; Manning and DuBois, 1962; Duncanson, 1966).

Another approach has investigated the possibility that there may be ability *factors* common to different kinds of learning tasks.

Twenty-seven memory tests and thirteen aptitude tests were given to 442 air cadets and a factor analysis made of the data. The materials, some presented visually and some auditorily, included numbers, letters, nonsense syllables, limericks, stories, pictures, and designs. The following kinds of memory were revealed: (1) *rote*, the recall of meaningless material; (2) *meaningful*, the recall of meaningful material; (3) *span*, the recall of a series of unrelated items presented only once. Whether the materials were presented by sight or sound, the same capacity was required. The meaningful memory ability was the same for both verbal and nonverbal materials.°

Do slow learners remember better?

We have all heard someone say, "I'm slow to learn, but I never forget." Contrary to popular opinion, however the slow learner does not remember better than the fast learner. Although it might appear that slow learners, because they go over the simpler parts of a task so many more times, would recall them better than the fast learners, this hypothesis was not supported in a recent study.

Elementary school children learned to associate geometric figures with numbers and were then divided into groups on the basis of how fast they had learned. After twenty-four hours they were required to relearn the material. The fast group took fewer trials to relearn and made fewer errors than did the slow group.†

There is a considerable body of data consistent with these findings, starting with a study that was published over seventy years ago (Calkins, 1894).

Can ability be increased through learning?

We can learn not only how to do or say specific things but also *how to learn*, and this kind of past learning is important in determining our ability to learn at any given time. This fact was clearly demonstrated in an experiment which is considered a classic.

°Adapted from "A Factor Analysis of Memory Ability," unpublished doctoral dissertation, Princeton University, H. P. Kelley, 1954.
†Adapted from "The Relative Retentive Abilities of Fast and Slow Learners" by Gregory and Bunch. Paper presented at the Midwestern Psychological Association Meetings, 1956.

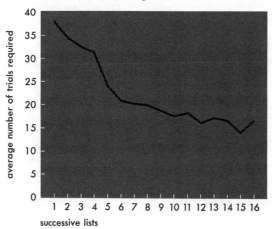

Table P1.1.　Learning how to learn

average number of trials required (y-axis)

successive lists (x-axis)

Based on Ward, 1937

College students were given sixteen lists of nonsense syllables to learn to the point that each syllable could be spelled correctly before it was exposed on a memory drum. The lists were equivalent in difficulty, and in the similarity of the items to each other within the list. The results are clearly seen in Table Pl.1. The number of trials required to learn the final lists was about one half as great as that required to learn the first list.‡

Learning to learn is even more pronounced with highly meaningful material. For example, you have undoubtedly learned a great deal about how to learn college subject matter in the most efficient manner. Perhaps you have learned how to organize and categorize new ideas and distinguish between central points and subordinate ones. Undoubtedly you have also learned certain basic concepts in introductory courses that you have used and built upon in more advanced courses. Without these basic concepts and general study skills, you probably would not have had the ability to master the advanced work, however good your genetic potential.

Psychologists would say you have been forming *learning sets* which enable you to learn more rapidly and understand more advanced material. In recent years, systematic studies of the formation of learning sets have been made with both animal and human subjects.

A series of ingenious studies by Harry Harlow first demonstrated this kind of learning.

In these studies monkeys were presented with a series of problem situations in which the principle was always the same but the specific material was varied. In each problem two geometric forms were presented. A reward was always hidden under the

‡Adapted from "Reminiscence and Rote Learning" by L. B. Ward, *Psychological Monographs*, Vol. 49, No. 4 (1937).

175

Figure P1.1 and Table P1.2. The Establishment of Learning Sets. The photo shows Harlow's apparatus and the kind of geometric forms used in the problems. The graph contrasts the learning curves for early and late problems.

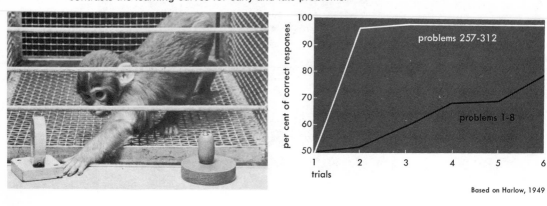

Based on Harlow, 1949

same one, but the position, size, and color of the forms were varied. When one problem was mastered, a new problem with different forms was presented. Altogether 344 problems were used.

In the early problems several trials were necessary for mastery, but by the 257th problem the monkeys had apparently learned the general rule; if they picked the wrong form on the first trial, they picked the right one on the second trial and consistently thereafter 98 percent of the time. A comparison of the shapes of the two learning curves shows the monkeys' increased ability to solve problems of this type. (See Figure Pl.1 and Table Pl.2.) On the early problems the usual learning curve was obtained, showing gradual learning over many trials; on the later problems the subjects needed only one trial to discover which item of each new pair was the correct one. (The learning curves start at 50 percent correct responses because prior to learning there would be as many correct responses as errors just by chance.)

Following this series learning-set formation on more complex problems was tested by putting the same monkeys through a series of 112 discrimination reversal problems. In each of these, a discrimination problem was presented for 7, 9, or 11 trials; these were followed by 8 more trials in which the previously correct stimulus became the incorrect one and vice versa. By the 70th problem and thereafter, performance on the second reversal trial was 97 percent accurate. Thus, not only were the animals performing as well as they had on the original problems, but they had formed the new learning set for reversal more rapidly than the original one, even though it was more complex. Evidently the monkeys were learning how to learn learning sets.§

A similar pattern of learning-set formation has been found in children of nursery-school age, in studies using beads or toys as rewards—although children, of course, are quicker than monkeys to learn the important relationships. Previously acquired learning sets tend to become increasingly important as the learning task becomes more complicated.

§Adapted from "The Formation of Learning Sets" by H. F. Harlow, *Psychological Review*, Vol. 56 (1949), 51–65.

176

A recent study with seventh-grade subjects sought to analyze the influence of previously acquired learning sets on speed of mastery in a course on equation solving.

In this study it was discovered that a subject's ability to learn to solve linear equations depended primarily upon how well he had acquired a whole hierarchy of learning sets. This hierarchy was revealed by asking, "What would an individual have to know how to do in order to perform this task?" In order to multiply, for example, he would need to know the multiplication table. Before that he would need to know how to read numbers and multiplication signs, have concepts of "five-ness," "eight-ness," and so on.

This study found a consistently high relationship between success on relevant subordinate learning sets and on higher learning sets. As the subjects progressed from the bottom to the top of the hierarchy, their rate of learning new sets depended increasingly on the learning sets previously acquired and decreasingly upon basic ability factors.[11]

These findings show that, as material to be learned becomes more complex, the rate of learning depends increasingly upon whether the individual has previously built up the necessary subordinate sets or must acquire them all in the current learning situation. The more learning sets he has in his repertoire, the greater his ability to tackle complex problems.

How does learning ability change with age?

Teachers, students, and parents are all interested in knowing at what age one should attempt to learn certain things in order to achieve maximum returns on a minimum investment of time and effort. And since social statistics show that the proportion of elderly people in our population is continually growing, it is becoming increasingly important to investigate the extent to which aging affects the ability to learn.

In general, studies with many kinds of learning tasks have shown that the quality of learning performance increases during childhood and up to maturity, but that after this time both speed and accuracy of learning decline. Part of this change with age may be attributable to factors other than learning capacity. For example, during childhood and adolescence a growing background of experience undoubtedly contributes to improved performance, whereas in old age a poor score in learning or recall may reflect poor motivation or a decrease in visual acuity or motor coordination (Hovland, 1951). or motor coordination (Hovland, 1951).

The exact course of the rise and fall in learning performance seems to depend on the nature of the material to be learned.

---

[11]Adapted from "Abilities and Learning Sets in Knowledge Acquisition" by R. M. Gagné and N. E. Paradise, *Psychological Monograph*, Vol. 75 (1961), p. 14.

In a series of experiments, a group of subjects aged about twenty and another group over sixty learned two motor and three verbal tasks. One of the motor tasks was learning to perform a coordinated movement of the right hand while looking directly at it. The other motor task was learning to perform the same type of movement when the hand was seen in a mirror. Notice that in the first of these tasks the habits of a lifetime were useful—many of the basic elements of the required movement had been practiced in random fashion through daily manipulation of objects. In the second task, however, old visual habits would actually interfere. Before the mirror-vision habit could be established, the old direct-vision habits had to be overcome. The results showed quite clearly that the older learners were more handicapped than the younger ones in this mirror-vision learning task.

The three verbal tasks showed comparable results. The tasks were the following:
1. Associating meaningful pairs of words, such as horse-sheep.
2. Associating nonsense materials, such as $F \times P = V$.
3. Associating interference materials, such as $2 \times 4 = 9$.

In each case the subjects learned to give the second member of the pair upon seeing the first. Notice that the meaningful words can be grouped by some logical principle—both words in the example are names of animals that eat grass. But the nonsense materials are purely arbitrary; $F \times P$ could equal V or it could equal anything else. The third pair, the interference material, is so labeled because old verbal habits interfere with learning. We are so used to thinking and saying 8 when we see 2×4 that it is very hard to learn to say 9.

On all three tasks the young group was superior to the older one. The differences were least for the meaningful pairs of words and greatest for the interference materials. Again, performance on tasks in which prior learning was an aid showed a smaller decrement with age than performance on new tasks which conflicted with older habits.[°]

Several other factors in the intellectual decline of the aged were investigated in a more recent study which used subjects of at least high-average intelligence.

Two hundred subjects were divided into three age groups matched for general intelligence, vocabulary, and social background as measured by education and occupational history. Group A consisted of persons aged 17 to 35; Group B, 36 to 55; and Group C, 56 to 74. Their performances were compared for several different types of learning.

Ability to repeat digits spoken by the experimenter did not decline appreciably with the age of the group, but the older group did more poorly than the younger groups in repeating digits backward. Their visual memory was even more impaired, as shown by a test in which they looked for one minute at a card containing ten geometric shapes and then tried to identify those ten on a card containing twenty shapes. There was also considerable age decrement in incidental, or latent, learning—the ability to notice and remember things which are not immediately relevant to the task in hand.

In tests of rote learning of nonsense syllables, it was found that all groups were equally subject to the serial position effect (greater ease in recalling early than later items in a series and greatest difficulty of all with those just past the middle of the list). The men's performance on rote learning did not decline until the late sixties, whereas some decrement was seen in the women as early as the forties. Except for this earlier decrement of the women in rote learning and a decrement of Group B as a whole on the incidental learning tasks, the differences between Groups A and B were slight.[°°]

[°]From "The Method of Common Points of Mastery as a Technique in Human Learning Experimentation" by F. L. Ruch, *Psychological Review*, Vol. 43 (1936), 229–234.
[°°]Adapted from "Some Effects of Age on Short-term Learning and Remembering" by D. B. Bromley, *Journal of Gerontology*, Vol. 13 (1958), 398-406.

A slightly different approach to learning and aging was made in another recent study of short-term retention of rapidly changing information.

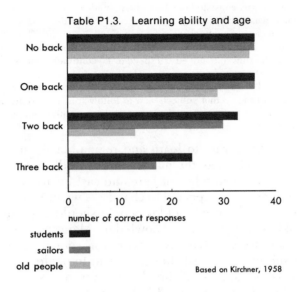

Table P1.3. Learning ability and age

number of correct responses

students

sailors

old people
Based on Kirchner, 1958

The apparatus consisted of twelve telegraphic keys, numbered 1 to 12, with lights directly above them, also numbered 1 to 12. Light moved from key to key at a fixed speed and a buzzer sounded when a correct response was made. Keys were pressed under four conditions: (a) no-back, in which the subject pressed the key where the light appeared: (b) one-back, in which he pressed the key where the light had just gone out; (c) two-back, in which he pressed the key where the light had gone out two positions before; and (d) three-back, in which he pressed the key where the light had been three positions before. Subjects included twenty persons aged 60 to 84 and twenty aged 18 to 24 (ten sailors and ten college psychology students).

The elderly subjects did about as well as the young ones in the no-back condition, showing that they were able to keep up with the physical movement of the light. However, they showed a serious decline in performance under the other conditions. (See Table P1.3.) While the students made a mean of 36.00 correct responses on one-back (the same as their no-back mean), older subjects made a mean of only 29.33 correct responses. Under two-back conditions, the elderly group made only 12.58 correct responses as compared to 32.90 for the students. Furthermore, only about half of the total number of key pressings made by the elderly group on two-back were correct, as against 90 per cent of those made by the sailors, who were slightly less efficient than the students. Older subjects tended to omit many responses altogether under the more complex conditions, whereas younger ones usually managed to respond, even if inaccurately. When given more time for the two-back condition, four older subjects approached the scores made by the younger ones in the regular length of time allowed. Since the elderly subjects had shown ability to keep up with the light physically, the differences apparently reflected ability to retain and organize information about the light.††

---

††Adapted from "Age Differences in Short-term Retention of Rapidly Changing Information" by W. K. Kirchner, *Journal of Experimental Psychology*, Vol. 55 (1958), 352–358.

Similar results were obtained in a study involving ability of elderly people to perform a pursuit tracking task after the course had disappeared from view.

The apparatus consisted of a box with a window showing a moving paper on which the course was marked. The subject was to follow the course with a pen which he moved by means of a wheel at the bottom of the apparatus. The older subjects (aged 46 to 56) did about as well as the younger ones (aged 21 to 28) when the course remained in view all the time and moved at a speed of 4.5 centimeters per second, but made more errors when the speed was increased to 9 centimeters per second. The difference in performance between young and old was much greater when the course was masked from time to time so that subjects had to follow it as they remembered it. Errors for both age groups increased as the amount of information which had to be stored increased, but the increase was more severe for older subjects.‡‡

Since the ability to learn and remember is an important part of general intelligence, the many broader studies of age changes in intelligence are also relevant here and cast further light on how learning ability can be expected to change as we grow older. It seems that there is no reason why older people should give up trying to learn new skills and gain new knowledge. Many people look forward to retirement from active business or professional life as an opportunity to pursue interests that they have had to neglect during their working years. In general, if the elderly person is sufficiently motivated, he will not be disappointed in his progress as long as the new skills he tries to learn are not in conflict with older ones.

The decreased ability of older people to acquire knowledge, skills, and attitudes that are inconsistent or antagonistic to what they have previously learned and practiced, may help to account for the well-known fact that people tend to become conservative or even reactionary as they grow older. Although our society is rapidly changing, both in technology and in prevailing economic philosophy, requiring new attitudes and skills, it can be predicted that an aging businessman will come more and more to react to new problems on the basis of knowledge, skills, and attitudes learned in his youth. Thus a certain degree of conservatism would appear to be part of the biological and social heritage of mankind. ◀

1. What is the chapter about? _____

_____

2. This chapter is divided into how many sections?
   a. three   b. four   c. five   d. six
3. T or F: Ability can be increased through learning sets.
4. T or F: The ability to learn and remember is an important part of general intelligence.
5. List at least four questions you would read to answer if you were to read this chapter closely for class.

---

‡‡Adapted from "Age Change and Information Loss in Performance of a Pursuit Tracking Task Involving Interrupted Preview" by S. Griew, *Journal of Experimental Psychology*, Vol. 55 (1958), 486–689.

PRACTICE **4**

Directions. Explore the following lab-manual exercise as you were shown in Chapters 1 and 2. After exploring, you should be able to tell what materials you will need, the purpose of the experiment, and what you are expected to do. When you have finished exploring the lab-manual assignment, answer the questions which follow without referring back. Check your answers on p. 249.

► Tissues and Organs[4]

A. *The fundamental tissues of animals*

All animal tissues may be classified as belonging to one of four fundamental tissues: epithelial, connective, muscular, or nervous. Blood is sometimes thought of as a circulating connective tissue, and reproductive cells (eggs and sperm) as a variety of epithelial tissue. These two are, however, sometimes regarded as sufficiently different and important to merit separate classification. Under the latter system, six tissues are distinguished: epithelial, connective, muscular, nervous, reproductive and vascular (blood). The last two will be studied later.

1. Epithelial Tissue

The outer surfaces of animals as well as all internal surfaces (tubules, ducts, cavities) are covered by compactly arranged sheets of cells known as *epithelia* (singular: epithelium). An epithelium is a layer of closely compacted cells with a free surface. Examples of epithelial tissue (frog skin and inner lining of the cheek) have already been seen in Exercise 1, Sec. B, 3.

2. Connective Tissue

All of the supporting and "packing" tissue of the body is classified as connective tissue. It forms, in its various differentiations, bones and cartilage, tendons and ligaments, the dermis, and the inner and outer framework of all organs except the brain and spinal cord.

On a prepared slide of connective tissue, notice the fine wavy bundles of *fibrous connective tissue* and the thicker straight fibers of *elastic connective tissue*. Fibers of these two kinds, interwoven to form a meshwork, are found in varying relative proportions in most connective tissues. Can you suggest what their mechanical functions may be? Are the fibers formed within cells? (See textbook.) The cytoplasm of connective tissue cells takes no stain in ordinary preparations. Hence only their nuclei are visible in your slides.

---

[4]DuShane and Regnery, *op. cit.*, pp. 9–10.

Look at a slide containing sections of cartilage (gristle). The cells are separated from one another by a firm elastic matrix produced by the activities of the cells. The cells may be somewhat shrunken, although in life they fill the cavities in the matrix. Connective tissue fibers are present in the matrix but are visible only after special treatment. Where does cartilage occur in the body? What is its mechanical function?

3. Muscular Tissue

There are three kinds of muscular or contractile tissues: *striated, smooth* and *cardiac*. The large muscles that move parts of the skeleton are striated; those in the walls of hollow organs (digestive system, glands, blood vessels) are smooth; and those of the heart are branched and striated to form a special kind of muscle, cardiac muscle, found nowhere else in the body.

Take a very small piece of fresh muscle (striated) from the leg of a frog. Tease it apart in physiological salt solution with dissecting needles to isolate the fibers. Add methyl green to stain nuclei, cover, and observe. Each *muscle fiber* contains many smaller elements, the *muscle fibrils*. Scattered among the fibrils are many ovoid nuclei not separated from one another by cell membranes. Each muscle fiber is regarded as a single multinucleate cell, the fibrils as cytoplasmic inclusions. This kind of muscle is named from the clear markings or striations produced by the fibrils. These run at right angles to the long axis of the fiber.

Sketch and label a muscle fiber. Look at a prepared slide of isolated smooth muscle cells. They are spindle-shaped single cells.

4. Nervous Tissue

Look at a cross-section of the spinal cord of a frog or cat. Find the large nerve cells in the ventral part of the cord. Identify cell body, nucleus, and some of the nerve cell processes (axons and dendrites). ◄

1. Which of the following will you need for conducting the experiment?

a. microscope
b. prepared slides of epithelial tissue
c. prepared slides of connective tissue
d. prepared slides of blood tissue
e. prepared slides of muscular tissue
f. prepared slides of nervous tissue
g. physiological salt solution
h. a frog's leg

2. What other materials will you need for the experiment not listed above? _____

3. The purpose of the experiment is
   a. to classify frog tissues.
   b. to classify animal tissues into four fundamental ones.
   c. to classify the difference between egg and sperm cells.

4. T or F: You will be required to answer questions about your experiment on separate paper.

PRACTICE **5**

Directions. Explore the following article from a science magazine. Do not read the entire article. Explore it using the following steps you were shown in Chapter 2. (See p. 25.) You may want to time yourself to see how long it takes you to explore this article. A good rate would be anything under 60 seconds.

When you have finished exploring, answer the questions that follow the article without referring back. Check your answers on p. 249.

► ## Musical Flames May Test Engines, Rockets[5]

Carl Behrens

More than 100 years ago physicist John Leconte, noting that a gas flame at a concert jumped in time with certain notes from a cello, asserted that "we must look on all jets as musically inclined."

Since that time experimenters have shown that flames can actually accept and reproduce sound and music, acting as loudspeakers. Their experiments aimed sound waves at the flame, which picked them up and amplified them.

Now engineers at United Technology Center in Sunnyvale, Calif., have carried the idea a step further, and made a flame from a welding torch convert electric signals directly into sound. The setup can fill a large room with music or speech.

The prospect of welding-flame woofers and tweeters replacing the traditional paper cone loudspeakers in the hi-fi rig is remote, says UTC's Dr. A. G. Cattaneo, despite the apparently high fidelity of the flame's reproduction. The complex flame system wouldn't add anything that couldn't be done more easily with conventional speakers.

But a more sophisticated development of the principle could be used for a number of important engineering applications, including cutting down noise from jet engines, he says. The additional sound energy might be used to detune the flame noise so it doesn't resonate with the engine housing.

The principle of electrically affecting a flame has been known for some time, according to Dr. Robert M. Fristrom of Johns Hopkins University's Applied Physics Laboratory, a center of flame research.

Figure P1.2. Flame produces hi-fi sound

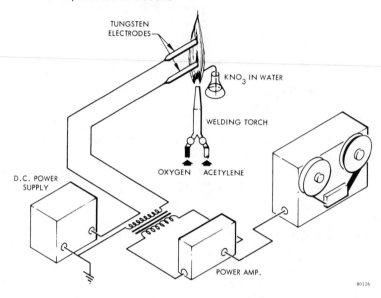

In a flame, the heat turns gas molecules into plasma, separating the electrons and the positive ions. If an electric field is applied, the electrons rush toward the positive pole and the ions move toward the negative pole. But since the ions are much heavier than the electrons, there is a net force in the direction of the negative pole, and the flame is bent by the electric field.

If the electric field is varied, as in an experiment Dr. Cattaneo reported in the Nov. 18 NATURE, then the flame moves in time with the variations, just as the cone in a loudspeaker moves in response to an electrical signal. And the movement of the flame causes sound waves just the way a loudspeaker makes them.

Imposing sound pressure within a burning flame might be a way of cutting jet noise, says Dr. Fristrom, because the burning rate of a gas is affected by pressure. If the burning rate happens to match the time it takes for the flame to fill the burning chamber, the flame noise resonates in the chamber. This acoustic loading, as it is called, contributes a large share of jet noise.

By detuning the burning rate through modifying sound pressure, the resonance noise might be cut out. Dr. Fristrom suggests that a sensor could put out a signal each time the resonance threatened to become serious, triggering the generator to alter the flame's sound output.

A big problem in such speculation, says Dr. Fristrom, is the amount of sound energy needed to shift the burning rate enough to be effective. That kind of question can only be worked out with experience, he says.

184

Another application that Dr. Cattaneo suggests is testing new rocket designs.

If a chemical rocket flame becomes unstable, it can shake the rocket apart. In order to test rockets for a tendency to become unstable, an explosive charge is set off in the chamber while the rocket is burning. The charge generates sound waves that could upset the rocket flame if it is vulnerable that way.

With the single charge, however, there is no control over the frequency of the sound imposed, says Dr. Cattaneo, and some frequencies can be more important than others.

With the proposed sound generator, the tester could scan over the whole range of frequencies, giving a much more complete test.

Not only does a flame vibrate with sounds; the movement is reflected in its output of light, reports Dr. Cattaneo. An image of the flame was aimed at a photocell connected through an amplifier to a loudspeaker. When music was imposed on the flame, it flickered; the flickering was picked up by the photocell and the music was reproduced by the loudspeaker.

"This is real basic research," says Dr. Cattaneo. "These effects have not really been taken into account before." ◄

Exploring time: _____

1. The basic idea of this article is that
   a. musical flames may test engines and rockets.
   b. gas flames jump in time with musical notes.
   c. flames can convert electric signals into sound which may be used in a number of engineering feats.
2. The prospect of welding-flame woofers and tweeters replacing the traditional cone loudspeakers is
   a. highly probable in the future.
   b. highly improbable.
   c. in test stages at present.
3. The principle of using flames to convert electrical signals into sound could be used
   a. to cut down noise from jet engines.
   b. to replace electric generators.
   c. not mentioned.
4. One application of the flame principle suggested by Dr. Cattaneo is
   a. testing how sound can kill flames.
   b. testing new rocket designs.
   c. testing musical reproduction through flames.
5. Not only does a flame vibrate with sounds, but the
   a. light is affected.
   b. movement is reflected in its output of light.
   c. sound is not at all affected by the size of the flame.

185

NOTES

PRACTICES IN STEP

TWO

Check the Vocabulary

PRACTICE 1

Directions. Read the following paragraph noticing particularly the underlined words. Choose the correct definition for each underlined word as it is used in context. Refer back to the paragraph as you need to. Check your answers on p. 250.

▶   Some substances are compounds: they are capable of being decomposed into simpler substances. Water can be broken down into its constituents, hydrogen and oxygen, but the latter two materials are elements, which cannot be decomposed further. In order to indicate the composition of a compound, a **formula** is written (e.g., H_2O). The formula, utilizing symbols and subscripts, provides the following information: (1) the elements in the compound; (2) the relative number of each atom (subscripts indicate the number of atoms, the number 1 being omitted); (3) the combining weights of the elements, since the symbol refers to an atom and the atomic weights are known; and (4) the molecular weight of the compound, if it is known.[1] ◀

Circle the correct response according to the way the word is used in context.

1. *compounds*
   a. powdered substance
   b. made of two or more parts
   c. a compromise
2. *decomposed*
   a. to break up
   b. to rot
   c. to let air out
3. *constituents*
   a. persons who vote

   b. costive ingredients
   c. components
4. *subscripts*
   a. symbols
   b. written underneath
   c. foreign words
5. *relative*
   a. comparative
   b. a relation
   c. subordinate

[1]Muller, *op cit.*, p. 28.

NOTES

PRACTICE **2**

Directions. Read the following paragraph noticing the underlined words. Choose the correct definition for each underlined word as it is used in context. Check your answers on p. 250.

▶   Adaptation is so universal in nature and is so clearly involved in differences between <u>subspecies</u> that it is a reasonable conclusion that many differences between human races were originally <u>adaptive</u>. (This does not exclude the probability that some arose from <u>random</u> fluctuations of gene frequencies in small groups of primitive men.) That has been hard to check, however, one way or another. There is good, but inconclusive, evidence that differences in skin color were adaptive when and where they arose. The color of the earliest men, doubtless <u>variable</u> as color is in all races, probably ranged through shades of brown. Darker or black skin was perhaps an adaptation in regions of damaging ultraviolet solar radiation, and lighter or white skin an adaptation to regions where that radiation (which is beneficial in *small* amounts) was deficient. Such genetic changes under the influence of selection take long periods of time. Whites have not been in Africa or Negroes in America nearly long enough for selection to have made a perceptible difference in their skin color. Is white or black skin more "primitive"? Which is "better"? Neither is more primitive than the other. Each was adaptively better under different conditions when and where it arose. Neither one seems to have a biological advantage under present conditions.[2] ◀

1. *subspecies*
   a. below level
   b. a division of species
   c. one under the other
2. *adaptive*
   a. reflective
   b. changeable
   c. corrosive

3. *random*
   a. haphazard
   b. shielded
   c. impetuous
4. *variable*
   a. truth
   b. unchangeable
   c. fluctuating

---

[2]Simpson and Beck, *op. cit.*, p. 687.

NOTES

PRACTICE **3**

Directions. Below is a list of Greek roots and their meanings. Use it to define the words which follow the list. Don't use a dictionary until you have tried to define the words by examining their Greek roots. Check your answers on p. 250. Use a dictionary for words you still don't understand.

acou	to hear	*helio*	sun
auto	self	*hemo*	blood
anti	against	*hydro*	water
arthr	joint	*itis*	inflammation of
anthrop	man, mankind	*macro*	large
bio	life	*meter*	measure
cardi	heart	*micro*	small
cephal	head	*neuro*	nerve
chlor	color	*octo*	eight
chron	time	*ost, osteo*	bone
cyt	cell	*patho*	disease of
derm	skin	*phobos*	fear
dia	across, apart	*poly*	many
epi	upon	*scope*	examine
gen	kinds, race	*som, somat*	body (sleep)
geo	earth	*thera*	to nurse
		zo	animals

1. acoustician _____
2. autogenesis _____
3. antibiotics _____
4. arthritis _____
5. anthropology _____
6. biochemistry _____
7. cardiac _____
8. cephalopod _____
9. chlorophyll _____
10. chronometer _____
11. cytology _____
12. diameter _____
13. epidermis _____
14. genetics _____
15. geophysics_____
16. hemorrhage _____
17. hydrometer _____

18. macrocosm _____
19. micrometer _____
20. neurology _____
21. octagon _____
22. osteopathy _____
23. anthropophobia _____
24. polygon _____
25. zoology _____

PRACTICE **4**

Directions. Below is a list of Latin roots and their meanings. Use it to define the words which follow the list. Use your dictionary only when you can't define a word by examining its Latin root. Check your answers on p. 251.

aqua	water	*mortis, mort*	death
audio	hear	*ocul*	eye
aur	ear	*ped*	foot
carn	flesh	*port*	carry
corpus	corpse, body	*post*	after
digit	finger, toe	*pro*	before
dorm	sleep	*sanguin*	blood
duc, duct	lead	*somn*	sleep
ex	out	*sol*	sun
locus	place	*son*	sound
mitto, mit	send	*video*	see

1. aquarium _____
2. audiology _____
3. audiogram _____
4. aural _____
5. carnivore _____
6. corpulent _____
7. digitate _____
8. dormant _____
9. aqueduct _____
10. conducive _____
11. exogen _____
12. locally _____
13. transmitter _____
14. mortuary _____
15. mortal _____
16. oculist _____
17. pedometer _____
18. portable _____
19. post-mortem _____
20. prophecy _____
21. prognosis _____
22. sanguine _____
23. somnambulist _____
24. solar _____
25. video tape _____

NOTES

PRACTICE **5**

Directions. Below are six questions followed by a sample page from a dictionary. Use the information contained in the dictionary page to answer the following questions. Check your answers on p. 251.

1. Find the definition for the word *biotherapy* and write it in the space below. _____
_____

2. From what language is the word derived? _____

3. What are the two major word parts and what do they mean? _____
_____

4. What is a *bioscope*? _____

5. What is *bioscopy*? _____

6. What is the difference between *bi* and *bio*? _____
_____

7. What is another word for *bionomics*? _____

8. What does *nomos* mean in Greek? _____

9. What is *bionomy*? _____

10. Judging from this one column from the dictionary, how important would you say the learning of Greek and Latin roots is for enlarging your vocabulary? _____

▶ **bi·ol·y·sis** (bī-ol'ə-sis), *n.* [*bio-* + *-lysis*], the destruction of life, as by bacteria or other microorganisms.

bi·o·lyt·ic (bī'ə-lit'ik), *adj.* of or produced by biolysis.

bi·o·met·rics (bī'ə-met'riks), *n.pl.* [construed as sing.], [< *bio-* + *metric*], that branch of biology which deals with its data statistically and by quantitative analysis.

bi·om·e·try (bī-om'ə-tri), *n.* [*bio-* + *metry*], 1. calculation of the probable human life span. 2. biometrics.

Bi·on (bī'ən), *n.* Greek pastoral poet; c. 3d century B.C.

bi·o·nom·ics (bī'ə-nom'iks), *n.pl.* [construed as sing.], [*bionomy* + *-ics*], the branch of biology that deals with the adaptation of living things to their environment; ecology.

bi·on·o·my (bī-on'ə-mi), *n.* [*bio-* + Gr. *nomos*, law], 1. the science that deals with the natural laws controlling life processes. 2. bionomics.

bi·o·phys·i·cal (bī'ō-fiz'i-k'l), *adj.* of biophysics.

195

bi·o·phys·ics (bī'ō-fiz'iks), *n.pl.* [construed as sing.], the branch of physics that deals with living matter.

bi·o·plasm (bī'ō-plaz'm), *n.* living matter; protoplasm.

bi·op·sy (bī'op-si), *n.* [see BIO- & -OPSIS], in medicine, the excision of a piece of living tissue for diagnostic examination by microscope, etc.

bi·o·scope (bī'ə-skōp'), *n.* [*bio* + *-scope*], a motion-picture projector.

bi·os·co·py (bī-os'kə-pi), *n.* [*bio-* + *-scopy*], in *medicine*, examination to find out whether life is present.

-bi·o·sis (bī-ō'sis, bi-ō'sis), [< Gr. *biōsis*, way of life < *bios*, life], a combining form meaning *a* (specified) *way of living*, as in *symbiosis*.

bi·o·so·cial (bī'ō-sō'shəl), *adj.* of the communal or family relationships of animals, as bees, apes, etc.

bi·o·stat·i·cal (bī'ō-stat'i-k'l), *adj.* of biostatics.

bi·o·stat·ics (bī'ō-stat'iks), *n.pl.* [construed as sing.], [*bio-* + *statics*], the branch of physiology that deals with the relation of structure to function in plants and animals: opposed to *biodynamics*.

bi·o·ta (bī-ō'tə), *n.* [see BIOTIC], the plant and animal life of a region.

bi·o·ther·a·py (bī'ō-ther'ə-pi), *n.* [*bio-* + *therapy*], the treatment of disease by means of substances secreted by or derived from living organisms, as serums, vaccines, bile, penicillin, etc.

bi·ot·ic (bī-ot'ik), *adj.* [Gr. *biōtikos* < *bios*, life], of life; of living things.

bi·ot·i·cal (bī-ot'i-k'l), *adj.* biotic.

bi·o·tin (bī'ə-tin), *n.* [*biotic* + *-in*], a bacterial growth factor, $C_{10}H_{16}O_3N_2S$, found in liver, egg yolk, and yeast; vitamin H: the lack of it may cause dermatitis.

bi·o·tite (bī'ə-tīt'), *n.* [after J. B. *Biot* (1774-1862), Fr. naturalist], a dark-brown or black mineral of the mica family, found in igneous and metamorphic rocks.

bi·o·type (bī'ō-tīp'), *n.* [*bio-* + *-type*], a group of plants or animals with similar hereditary characteristics.

bi·pa·ri·e·tal (bī'pə-rī'ə-t'l), *adj.* of or connected with the prominent rounded part of the two parietal bones.

bi·pa·rous (bip'ə-rəs), *adj.* [*bi-* + *-parous*], 1. bearing two offspring at a birth. 2. in *botany*, dividing into two branches.

bi·par·ti·san (bī-pär'tə-z'n), *adj.* of, having members from, or representing two parties.[3] ◄

The following exercises can help you develop rapid recognition of science words, develop your left-to-right eye movement, and generally overcome slow mechanical reading motions. Time the exercises.

Directions. When you are ready to be timed, look at the key word in the column on the left. Then quickly underline that word when it appears among the words on the right. Then go to the next word in the Key Word column. Do this for each word in the Key Word column as the example shows.

Key Word

cobalt	casium catalyst coburn <u>cobalt</u> cohere
gram	grain <u>gram</u> groin gypsum gene gold
anode	adenoid alkaline amino <u>anode</u> aero aorta

Work rapidly and try to finish the exercise in 25 seconds or less.

197

PRACTICE **6**

Begin timing

Key Word

1. helium	heredity	hormone	hybrid	helium	homo
2. electron	ecology	electron	electric	energy	ergot
3. density	diode	density	dynamo	dipole	Dacron
4. ecology	ecology	estrogen	esophagus	electron	endocrine
5. gravity	gene	garnet	galaxy	genetic	gravity
6. anode	algae	argon	aorta	anode	apogee
7. carbon	carbon	cancer	calcite	cardiac	cathode
8. anthropoid	anthropologist	antigen	antibiotic	anthropoid	
9. enzyme	embolism	enzyme	energy	ethyl	evaporate
10. antibody	antimony	antiseptic	antibody	antigen	aorta
11. cell	cyst	curie	cellulose	chitin	cell
12. gram	gram	graphite	gonad	gold	goiter
13. fissure	fission	fetus	femur	fissure	friction
14. calorie	cargon	cargonate	calcium	calorie	cell
15. asteroid	astronaut	astronomy	arsenic	asteroid	argon
16. diode	density	detergent	diode	diabetic	DNA
17. fetus	fungus	fetus	femur	fusion	fluorides
18. cobalt	cretin	cortisone	cobalt	corona	coburn
19. cretin	cretaceous	cosmic	cretin	crystal	cycles
20. diabetic	dialysis	diabetic	dolomite	density	diode

Time:_____ Check each row for accuracy. Errors:_____

Now look up in the Key Word column each word you didn't know and use one of the methods described in Chapter 4 for learning it.

PRACTICE 7

Directions. Follow the same directions as in the previous exercise.

Begin timing

Key Word

1. hydrogen	hydrocarbon	hydrology	hypothesis	hydrogen	
2. hyperplasia	hybrid	hormone	hyperplasia	homo sapiens	
3. cornea	corona	cortin	cortisone	cornea	curie
4. allergy	allergy	alloy	alkaloid	ammonia	algae
5. cholorine	cirrhosis	comet	concave	copper	chlorine
6. biocurrent	boric acid	bromine	bronchitis	biocurrent	
7. gland	gland	gamma	gastritis	genetic	gold
8. neuron	nerve	neutrino	neutron	neuron	nova
9. stethoscope	stratoscope	stethoscope	strontium	strain	
10. radium	reaction	reactor	radar	radio	radium
11. silicone	silica	serum	silicone	silver	shook
12. placenta	planet	plasma	platinum	placenta	physicist
13. osmosis	ossify	osmosis	ovum	ozone	orbit
14. isotope	iodine	iso-lucine	ion	isotope	iron
15. krypton	kilo	superman	kelp	krypton	krebs
16. metabolism	menopause	mason	meteor	mica	metabolism
17. photoelectric	photosphere	photoelectric	photon	phosphor	
18. spleen	spore	stapes	steroid	sonic	spleen
19. mastodon	mammoth	master	methane	mice	mastodon
20. larynx	larynx	laser	lava	lesser	liter	lipid

Time:_____ Check each row for accuracy. Errors:_____

Now look up in the Key Word column each word you didn't know and use one of the methods described in Chapter 4 for learning it.

PRACTICE **8**

Directions. Follow the same directions as in the previous exercise.

Begin timing

Key Word

1.	vestigial	vestigial vertebrate viable virus volt
2.	ultraviolet	ultrasonic universe ultraviolet vapor urea
3.	aeration	alternator anabolic ammonia aeration anode
4.	thyroid	theory torque thymus thyroid thalidomide
5.	tumor	tungsten turbine tumor trauma torque
6.	polymer	polymorphic polymer polyethylene positron
7.	sulfur	stress strain sunspots suture sulfur
8.	bacterium	barium barite battery bacterium beta
9.	centigrade	centimeter centigrade centrifuge center
10.	fluorides	frequency fluorescent fluorides fuel fetus
11.	electrode	electron electronic electricity electrode
12.	ozone	osmosis ozone ossify ovum orbit optic
13.	magnesium	magnetic malignant malleus magnesium mass
14.	parabolic	parabolic parametric paraplegic peptic
15.	ventricle	vaccination vitamin vacuum ventricle virus
16.	molecule	modulate molecule moraine mutation motor
17.	roentgen	rotation ribosomes rudidium radio roentgen
18.	slime	slate solar sonic spores slime stress
19.	neoplasm	nephritis neoplasm nerve nebula neuron

Time:_____ Check each row for accuracy. Errors:_____

Now look up in the Key Word column each word you didn't know and use one of the methods described in Chapter 4 for learning it.

PRACTICE **9**

Directions. Follow the same directions as in the previous exercise.

Begin timing

Key Word

1. nitrogen	niobium	niobium	nitroglycerine	nitrogen	
2. propane	primate	propane	protein	proton	pumice
3. viscera	virus	viscera	viable	Venus	vapor
4. zygote	zirconium	zinc	zygote	zoo	zymase
5. vascular	vascular	ventricle	viscera	vertebrate	
6. synapse	systolic	synthesize	stellar	sonic	synapse
7. sterile	steroid	sterile	stapes	spore	spleen
8. simian	seismic	silica	silver	simian	silicone
9. replicate	reproduction	reactor	replicate	retina	Rh
10. pupa	purine	pumice	pituitary	pupa	pitchblend
11. viscosity	vascular	viscosity	vaccination	vitamin	volt
12. spectrum	spectroscope	spermatozoa	speleology	spectrum	
13. volcanic	viscosity	volcanic	vain	victory	vertical
14. polyp	polymer	polarized	polyp	polymorphic	poly
15. biogenetic	biochemistry	biocurrent	biota	biogenetic	
16. plexus	plexiglas	plexus	plasma	plante	planet
17. satellite	satellite	saturated	sclerosis	serum	
18. refraction	reciprocate	resonance	retina	refraction	reactor
19. quartz	gravity	quartz	quarantine	squid	squirrel
20. plankton	planktonic	plague	plants	plankton	placebo

Time:_____ Check each row for accuracy. Errors:_____ Now look up
in the Key Word column each word you didn't know and use one of the
methods described in Chapter 4 for learning it.

PRACTICE **10**

Directions. Follow the same directions as in the previous exercise:

Begin timing

Key Word

1. pathology   pathogenic pathos pathology parabolic path
2. nuclear   nucleic acid nucleus nucleoprotein nuclear
3. mutant   mutant mutation muscle museums mushrooms
4. oxidation   oxygen oxygenated osmium oxidation orbit
5. isostasy   iso-lucine isotope iron ion isostasy
6. medusa   medulla mesoderm medusa metal man
7. biosphere   biocides biology biometry birds biosphere
8. mesophyte   mesoderm mesophyte metazoa metric micron
9. inertia   influence insect inertia insulin internal
10. linkage   link liver lizard linnaeus linkage
11. coenzyme   cortisone cosmic cytoplasm cyst coenzyme
12. leukemia   lead larva lethal leukemia lichen
13. nebulae   nucleus nebulae nitrogen nova nerve
14. isogamous   isogamy isolation isopters isogamous ion
15. colostrum   coleoptera colostrum colitis comet cloud
16. exosphere   exosphere experiment extrasensory exclusion
17. ingestion   inhibition insects infrared ingestion iodine
18. homosporous   homo-sapiens hormone homosporous horse
19. cyclones   cyclops cyclones cytology cytoplasm cyst
20. denaturation   detergent density dwarf deuterium denaturation

Time:_____ Check each row for accuracy. Errors: _____ Now look up in
the Key Word column each word you didn't know and use one of the
methods described in Chapter 4 for learning it.

PRACTICE **11**

Directions. Follow the same directions as in the previous exercise.

Begin timing

Key Word

1. hominoid	human homograft humoral humus hominoid
2. acid	algae actinomyces acid allergy alloy
3. fluoroscope	flora fluoroscope folic fermentation
4. combustion	commensal colloid coelom combustion clone
5. alcohol	alcohol albino analgesic apogamy ATP
6. heterosporous	heterogamous heterosomes heterosporous hypha
7. chlorophyll	cholesterol chromite chlorine chlorophyll
8. globulins	glomerulonephritis globulins glycerine gland
9. batholith	basophil batholith bathospere beta ray
10. glucose	glycerine globulins germs glucose gel
11. aurora	auricle aurora atropine atomic atom
12. herbivore	histamine hepatic heterosomes herbivore
13. barometer	barnacles base barometer batholith bake
14. gossamer	gonococus gross glycerine gyro gossamer
15. diaphragm	diabetes dialysis diaphragm devonian diode
16. phosphate	phosphorus phosphate phase petal petri
17. pseudopod	pseudocopulation pseudomonas pseudopod
18. testicle	testicle testes testicular tetanus test
19. atrophy	atropine atrophy atomics athletes ATP
20. circulation	cirrhosis circle circulate circulation

Time:_____ Check each row for accuracy. Errors:_____ Now look up in the Key Word column each word you didn't know and use one of the methods described in Chapter 4 for learning it.

THREE

Analyze for Comprehension

Introduction. In Section Three of this book, you were given explanations of some of the writing patterns that appear most often in science text-books. The following exercises are intended to help you learn to recognize those patterns as a means of increasing your comprehension powers.

You will remember that Chapters 5 through 10 deal with the following patterns:

Chapter 5	the classification pattern
Chapter 6	the process-description pattern
Chapter 7	the factual-statement pattern
Chapter 8	the problem-solving pattern
Chapter 9	the experiment-instructions pattern
Chapter 10	the combination of patterns

You may wish to reëxplore these chapters before attempting the exercises. However, you may be ready to begin right now.

You may time yourself as you read the selections in this section, but don't feel that you must. Each selection has the number of words counted and the formula for figuring out your rate, or the number of words per minute you read. Suppose you read a selection that is 900 words long in 120 seconds. Simply divide the number of seconds you read into the number of words in the article and multiply by 60. The multiplier 60 is used to convert seconds into words per minute as follows:

Words in selection: $\dfrac{900}{120} \times 60 = 450 \ wpm$
Reading time:

In all cases attempt to answer the questions which follow the reading selections without referring back to the selection. Some questions, by their nature, will require you to look back. If you miss a question, reread the selection to find the place where you misread the text and determine why you missed the question. Remember, doing these work pages is not as important as learning about your reading from doing them.

204

PRACTICE **1**

Directions. The following selection[1] is an example of the classification pattern discussed in Chapter 5. Preview it quickly, then read it carefully. Look for the main idea (what is being classified) and for the details used to develop the main idea (the classification breakdown).

Begin timing

►   Preceding chapters have shown how human beings constantly strive toward goals which gratify their biological and psychological needs. Sometimes people reach their goals with relative ease. But what happens when their needs are frustrated over a long period of time—that is, when they are prevented from reaching their goals?

Human adjustment is a never ending process of dealing with frustration. Serious frustrations of our biological drives have become relatively rare in the United States with its high level of prosperity and its ample welfare programs, but frustrations of our psychological and social needs have become even more common than they were in earlier times. Today we face business competition, marital problems, social laws and taboos, international tensions, and many other frustrations that are difficult to attack directly. And in our daily living we face one minor frustration after another—broken dates, late trains, blown fuses, fallen cakes, power failures, lost papers, absent friends, and so on and on.

How can we adjust to these constant frustrations? Sometimes we can overcome them, but sometimes we must yield to them, and often we must learn to live with them year in and year out.

Kinds of Frustration

The endless array of situations that block modern man's complex motives and produce frustrations may be classified into three main categories: *environmental, personal,* and *conflict.*

Environmental Frustrations

Our environment is full of obstacles that impede our progress. Our physical environment may frustrate us drastically at times through earthquakes, tornadoes, famines, or floods. It also provides innumerable petty frustrations—the barking dog that keeps us awake

---

[1]Ruch, *op. cit.,* pp. 461–462.

at night, the traffic jam, the uneven sidewalk that makes us stumble, the pen that will not write, or the rain at the ball game.

More serious, generally, are the obstacles provided by our social environment. Formal laws and social conventions prevent us from freely expressing many of our impulses. The man who has to work with unpleasant associates, the orphan cared for in the impersonal atmosphere of an institution, and the member of a minority group in a prejudiced community all suffer social frustrations.

Personal Frustration

An individual suffers personal frustration when he is prevented from realizing his ambitions by some personal limitation—either real or imagined. A boy who wants to play on the school basketball team may be thwarted by his lack of height. An individual who wants to go to a particular college may be thwarted by his inability to pass the entrance examination. Both physical and psychological barriers may be sources of personal frustration. For example, a boy may be shy because he feels that he is physically unattractive or because he feels that he lacks social skills.

Personal frustration frequently builds up *feelings of inferiority* and a felt lack of personal worth which, in turn, serve to increase the frustration. A questionnaire administered to a large group of college students showed that fewer than 10 per cent of the respondents had never experienced inferiority feelings about some aspect of their personal capacities—physical, social, intellectual, or moral (Allport, 1937). But college students as a group actually tend to be *superior* in all of these categories. Why, then, did they see themselves as inferior?

The answer to this paradox lies in the fact that feelings of inferiority are based not on actual inferiority but rather on one's *level of aspiration*. College students feel the need to compare themselves not to the population in general—to whom they are clearly superior—but to other college students (Festinger, 1954). If an individual's level of success in some activity falls below the level of the goal he has set for himself, he feels frustrated. Goals should be a challenge, but unrealistic expectations only invite failure and a feeling of inferiority.

Conflict Frustration

When an individual must choose one or the other of two goals or has both positive and negative feelings about a particular goal, he faces *conflict frustration*. Since motives may be either positive or negative—either seeking or avoiding—there are four possible types of conflict: *approach-approach, avoidance-avoidance, approach-avoidance,* and *double approach-avoidance.*

Approach-approach conflict. When the individual has two desirable but mutually exclusive goals, his situation is described as an *approach-approach conflict*. For example, a child holding a valued toy may see a kitten he wants to pet. In order to take up the kitten, he must put down the toy. At the adult level, a young man may want to marry and also to finish his education but, for financial reasons, not be able to do both. Conflicts of this type must usually be resolved by choosing one goal over the other, either excluding one entirely or deciding which to do first.

Avoidance-avoidance conflict. When the individual seeks to avoid two unpleasant alternatives but cannot directly avoid one without encountering the other, he is confronted with an *avoidance-avoidance conflict*. For example, a student may not want to do all the studying a course requires, but neither does he want to fail the course. Or he may want to avoid working with some person on a committee but not wish to offend him by saying so. Conflicts of this type are most often resolved by "leaving the field." In the first example, the individual might drop the course. In the second, he might resign from the committee and volunteer for a different activity.

Approach-avoidance conflict. In an *approach-avoidance conflict*, the individual is attracted to an object or state of affairs and simultaneously repelled by something associated with it. For example, a child may want to pick a water lily in a pond but be afraid to wade out to get it. Or a person may want to safeguard his health by going to the doctor for a physical checkup but fear the possible consequences of such a visit. The closer the individual gets to the goal, the more strongly he is repelled by the negative aspects associated with it. Approach-avoidance conflict usually produces indecision and vacillating behavior.

Double approach-avoidance. A more complex kind of conflict is *double approach-avoidance*, in which both courses of action have good and bad features which must be weighed in order for a choice to be made. For example, a salesman may have to decide between two jobs — one with a rather small territory in a pleasant climate but with lower pay and the other requiring more travel in a colder climate but allowing him to handle a product he especially enjoys selling. The resolution of this type of conflict involves the type of decision making described in Chapter 10.

There are both successful and unsuccessful ways of adjusting to any type of frustration. In the following sections we shall examine some of the most common reaction patterns. ◄

Words in selection: $\dfrac{1107}{} \times 60 =$ _____*wpm*
Reading time:

1. What is being classified? _____

2. What are the major subdivisions in the classification pattern?
   _____

3. Using the answers to questions 1 and 2, fill in the following diagram:

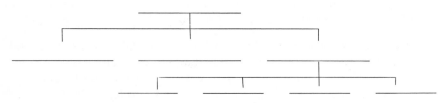

4. What are the four types of conflict frustration?
   a. _____
   b. _____
   c. _____
   d. _____

5. Complete the following classification diagram for the selection you have just read.

Check your answers on p. 252.

PRACTICE **2**

Directions. Read the following example of a process-description pattern. Look for the main idea (what the process is and how it works).

Begin timing

▶   The way in which bones grow can be determined by fastening small metal markers to the bones of a young animal, letting the animal grow for a while, and then determining the new positions of the markers. The outcome of such experiments is shown diagrammatically in Figure P3. 1*A, B*. Notice that, as growth proceeds, the spacing between markers 2, 3, and 4 remains the same, whereas the space between 1 and 2 increases, indicating that the region of growth is somewhere between markers 1 and 2. The growth region is, in fact, quite near the end of the bone.

Bones, however, grow not only in length but also in thickness. How is this accomplished? Again, an experiment with a metal marker answers our question. This time, a metal ring is fastened around a long bone of a very young animal. The subsequent positions are diagrammed in Figure P3.1*C-E*. Notice that the ring is first

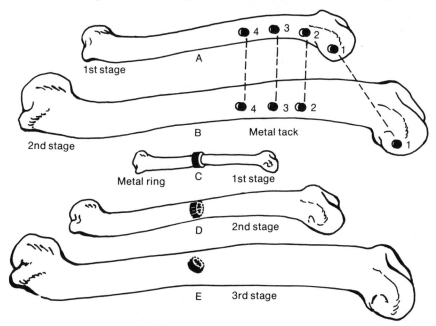

Figure P3.1. The experimental observations that reveal the location of the growing regions of a long bone. See text for discussions

209

covered over with bone, indicating that bone is added from the outside. Later, the ring appears free in the marrow cavity as the bone in which it was embedded is destroyed, thus making room for the enlarging marrow cavity.

Growth in thickness of the bone is brought about by a layer of tissue called the **periosteum** (Gr. *peri* = around + *osteon* = bone), a thin nonbony sheath that encircles the bone and lays down new bone on the outside. It can readily be understood how activity of the cells of the periosteum results in covering the ring with bone.

The freeing of the ring, as it appears in Figure P3.1E, is also the result of cellular activity. As the wall of a long bone increases in diameter, certain cells digest the bone on the inner surface of the cylinder, thus making room for the marrow, which also consists of cells and their products. Because the marrow is soft, the metal ring is no longer rigidly held in position once the bone has grown to a diameter greater than that of the ring.[2] ◄

Words in selection: $\frac{310}{}$ × 60 = _____ *wpm*
Reading time:

Answer the following questions. Check your answers on p. 252.
    1. What process is being described? _____
    _____
    2. How do bones grow?   _____
    _____
    _____
    _____
    3. Why is the ring in Figure P3.1 *E* free in the marrow?
    _____
    _____
    _____
    4. What does *periosteum* mean?   _____
    _____
    5. What is periosteum? _____
    _____

---

[2]Hardin, *op. cit.*, pp. 449–450.

PRACTICE **3**

Directions. Read the following example of a factual-statement pattern. Look for the main idea and the supporting statements of the passage.

Begin timing

▶   One of the most important of the properties of blood is its ability to *clot*, or **coagulate,** that is, to turn from a liquid to a firm solid. A few minutes after normal blood is shed from a blood vessel, it clots. Clotting at the site of the wound closes the opening and prevents further loss of blood. Were it not for this property of blood, the slightest wound might result in death. This danger is a very real one for certain rare individuals who suffer from a disease known as **hemophilia** (Gr. *hemo* = blood + *philos* = loving). The blood of hemophiliacs, though it will clot, clots so slowly that even a tiny cut constitutes a threat to life.

    On the other hand, it is equally important that blood not clot while still within a vessel. Under abnormal circumstances, blood may clot, forming a plug, or **thrombus** (Gr. from *trepho* = thicken), locally stopping the flow of blood. The resultant condition is known as **thrombosis** (the Greek suffix *-osis* indicates much, i.e., too much). If a clot is carried around in the blood stream and lodges in a vessel distant from its site of formation, it is called an **embolus** (Gr. plug). The seriousness of thrombosis or **embolism** depends on the vessels plugged. Coronary thrombosis may cause immediate death.[3] ◀

Words in selection: $\dfrac{215}{}$ × 60 = _____*wpm*
Reading time:

Answer the following questions. Check your answers on p. 253.
  1. The main idea of this passage is
    a. blood clots.
    b. hemophilia, thrombosis, and embolism are dangerous.
    c. the importance of coagulation.
  2. Define these words:
    a. coagulate _____

    _____

    b. hemophilia _____

    _____

_____

[3]*Ibid.*, p. 507.

211

c. thrombosis _____

_____

d. embolism _____

_____

3. Define these Greek roots and affixes:
    a. hemo _____
    b. philos _____
    c. trepho _____
    d. osis _____
    e. embolus _____
4. When does normal blood begin to clot after a cut?
    a. immediately
    b. a few seconds
    c. a few minutes

PRACTICE **4**

Directions. Read the following example of the problem-solving pattern, looking for the question.

Begin timing

►   Translocation of organic materials. It was established long ago, initially through some ingenious experiments performed by the great Italian biologist Malpighi in the seventeenth century, that the outer layer of conducting tissue in trees (the phloem) is responsible for the downward transport of materials produced in the leaves. The experiment is a simple one. A ring is cut into the bark around the stem or a branch, so that the externally located phloem is cut but the xylem layer is not interrupted. Gradually, organic materials accumulate *above* the ring but are depleted below it, showing that a downward pathway has been intercepted. If the cut is made deeper, into the sapwood of the tree so as to cut the xylem also, the leaves above the cut quickly wilt, showing that an upward route for water has been severed in addition. More recent evidence, using radioactive labeling of photosynthetic products with $C_{14}O_2$, has confirmed the old conclusion that they travel in phloem cells.[4] ◄

Words in selection: $\dfrac{165}{}$ × 60 = _____*wpm*
Reading time:

Now answer the following questions. Check your answers on p. 253.
   1. What is the main idea of this passage (or the problem that was solved)?
     a. The inner layer of conducting tissue is the phloem.
     b. The inner layer of conducting tissue is responsible for the transport of materials produced in leaves.
     c. The outer layer of conducting tissue is responsible for the transport of materials produced in leaves.
   2. Describe the experiment conducted to prove the main idea of the passage._____
_____
_____
_____

[4]From *The Biology of Organisms* by William H. Tefler and Donald Kennedy (New York: John Wiley & Sons, Inc., 1965), p. 236.

3. What happens if the cut is made deeper into the xylem?

_____

_____

_____

4. Who conducted the original experiment and when?

_____

5. What newer experiments have recently confirmed the seventeeth-century experiment? _____

_____

_____

PRACTICE **5**

Directions. Read the following example of a selection that uses a combination of patterns. This passage uses factual statements which define, compare, and contrast, plus a classification pattern.

Begin timing

▶   Nearly all the quantities in the physical world can be expressed in terms of only four fundamental measurements, those of length, mass, time, and electric current. Thus every unit of area (the square foot, for instance) is essentially the product of a length unit and a length unit, every unit of speed (the mile per hour, for instance) is a length unit divided by a time unit, every unit of force (the newton, for instance) is the product of a mass unit and a length unit divided by the square of a time unit, and every unit of electric charge (the coulomb, for instance) is a current unit multiplied by a time unit. A *system of units* is a set of specified units of length, mass, time, and electric current from which all other units are to be derived. All units are arbitrary, and in fact thousands of different ones have been used at one time or another in the course of history, but today only two systems of units are at all common. These are the *British system*, in which the units of length, mass, time, and electric current are respectively the foot, the slug, the second, and the ampere, and the *metric system*, in which the fundamental units in the same order are the meter, the kilogram, the second, and the ampere. (The familiar *pound* is actually a unit of force rather than of mass; the distinction will be discussed in Chapter 5.) The British system is used in commerce and industry in most English-speaking countries, while the metric system is used in the rest of the world and for all scientific work.[5] ◀

Words in selection: $\dfrac{276}{\text{Reading time:}} \times 60 = $ _____*wpm*

Now answer the following questions. Check your answers on p. 253.
   1. What is being classified? _____
_____

_____
[5]Beiser, *op. cit.*, p. 14.

2. What are the major subdivisions of the answer to Question 1?

_____

_____

3. What are the two systems of units used today?

_____

4. A system of units is
   a. a set of specified units of length, mass, time, and electric current.
   b. a set of specified units, respectively, the foot, the slug, the second, and the ampere.
   c. a set of specified units, respectively, the meter, the kilogram, the second, and the ampere.
   d. not discussed.

5. List the units of the following:

The British system	The Metric system
a. _____	a. _____
b. _____	b. _____
c. _____	c. _____
d. _____	d. _____

PRACTICE **6**

Directions. Read the following passage to determine the writing pattern, the main idea, and the supporting details.

Begin timing

►   In the first decades of the twentieth century, the individual gene, like the individual virus, could not be seen, and yet it could be worked with fruitfully. The key to such work came when the American geneticist, Thomas Hunt Morgan (1866–1945), introduced a new biological tool in 1907, a tiny fruit fly, *Drosophila melanogaster.* This was a small insect, capable of being bred in large numbers and with virtually no trouble. Its cells, moreover, possessed but four pairs of chromosomes.

    By following fruit-fly generations, Morgan discovered numerous cases of mutations, thus extending to the animal kingdom what De Vries had discovered among plants. He was further able to show that various characteristics were linked; that is, inherited together. This meant that the genes governing such characteristics were to be found on the same chromosome, and this chromosome was inherited, of course, as a unit.

    But linked characteristics were not eternally linked. Every once in a while, one was inherited without the other. This came about because pairs of chromosomes occasionally switched portions ("crossing over"), so that the integrity of an individual chromosome was not absolute.

    Such experiments even made it possible to locate the spot on the chromosome at which a particular gene might exist.[6] ◄

Words in selection: $\dfrac{210}{}$ × 60 = _____*wpm*
Reading time:

Now answer the following questions. Check your answers on p. 254.
1. The basic writing pattern is
    a. classification.
    b. process-description.
    c. experiment-instructions.
    d. problem-solving.

----

[6]Asimov, *op. cit.,* p. 166.

2. The main idea of this passage is that
   a. Morgan's experiments helped clarify how genes governing certain characteristics were inherited through certain chromosomes.
   b. experiments such as Morgan's made it possible to locate particular genes.
   c. in the first decades of the twentieth century, the individual gene could not be seen.
3. What was the "new biological tool" Morgan used in his experiments?

   _____

   _____

4. What is the importance of Morgan's experiments?

   _____

   _____

   _____

PRACTICE 7

Directions. Read the following selection and notice the writing pattern used, the main idea, and the important details.

Begin timing

▶   Many chemical reactions that proceed slowly if at all are speeded by the action of a **catalyst,** a substance that accelerates the process without itself undergoing permanent change or being used up. Inorganic hydrogen and oxygen gases, for example, when brought together do not react, but in the presence of finely divided (colloidal) platinum as a catalyst they combine to make water—with explosive violence. Catalysts are used much by industry as in the cracking of petroleum and many other processes. Complex organic catalysts, the **enzymes,** are universal in living matter. They are the essence of life because they promote a multitude of chemical reactions with great rapidity. Otherwise these reactions would proceed too slowly to maintain vital processes. A sugar such as glucose, exposed to oxygen in the air, undergoes scant change, but when in the cells of a living animal it is oxidized rapidly to yield energy.[7] ◀

Words in selection: $\dfrac{150}{}$ × 60 = _____*wpm*
Reading time:

Now answer the following questions. Check your answers on p. 254.
1. The basic writing pattern is
   a. process-description.   c. combination.
   b. factual-statement.   d. classification.
2. A catalyst is
   a. a chemical reaction.
   b. found in collodial platinum.
   c. a substance that accelerates a chemical reaction.
   d. much used by industry for the cracking of petroleum.
e. An enzyme is
   a. a chemical reaction.
   b. an organic catalyst.
   c. universal in processing petroleum.
   d. the essence of life.
4. Why are enzymes important to life?

_____

_____

---

[7]Storer and Usinger, *op. cit.,* p. 69.

219

FOUR

Synthesize for Understanding

Introduction. The following drills will give you practice in some of the stages of Step Four: *Synthesize for Understanding.* These exercises provide practices in notetaking, in marking, in locating information quickly from resource materials, and in putting all four steps together for a total reading process.

PRACTICE **1**

Directions. The following selection is much shorter than a typical reading assignment. However, it can serve as an example for you to begin practice on Step Four: *Synthesize for Understanding.* Explore the selection. Then read the passage carefully, marking where you think major ideas are, listing or commenting in the margin, and generally following the points listed in Chapter 11.

▶ Glaciers

In a cold climate with abundant snowfall, the snow of winter may not completely melt during the following summer, and so a deposit of snow accumulates from year to year. Partial melting and continual increase in pressure cause the lower part of a snow deposit to change gradually into ice. If the ice is sufficiently thick, gravity forces it to move slowly downhill. A moving mass of ice formed in this manner is called a *glacier.*

Existing glaciers are of two principal types. (1) Easily accessible glaciers—in the Alps, on the Alaskan coast, in the western United States—are patches and tongues of dirty ice lying in mountain valleys that are called *valley glaciers.* These move slowly down their valleys, melting copiously at their lower ends; the combination of downward movement and melting keeps their ends in approximately the same position from year to year. Movement in the faster valley glaciers (a few feet per day) is sufficient to keep their lower ends well below timber line. (2) Glaciers of another type cover most of Greenland and Antarctica: huge masses of ice thousands of square miles in area, engulfing hills as well as valleys, and appropriately called *icecaps.* These, too, move downhill, but the "hill" is the slope of their upper surfaces. An icecap has the shape of a broad dome, its surface sloping outward from a thick central portion of greatest snow accumulation; its motion is radially outward in all directions from its center.[1] ◀

Now answer the following questions without referring back.
1. Define glacier. _____
   _____
   _____

[1]Krauskopf and Beiser, *op. cit.*, p. 502.

2. How do glaciers form? _____ _____

_____

_____

3. Define the two principal types of glaciers. _____

_____

_____

Check your answers on p. 254. While there is no key for you to check your marking (everyone marks differently), your marking should have helped you answer the questions more easily.

PRACTICE **2**

Directions. Read the following selection from a science reference book. Do not mark on the passage, just as you would not mark in a library reference book. Instead, use a notebook. Then answer the questions which follow the article without referring back to it. Check your answers on p. 254.

► *Genetics.*[2]

Science concerned with the study of the inborn properties and the inborn differences which determine heredity. Such studies are closely linked with relevant subjects, such as cytology, reproduction, breeding, etc. It is evident that the implications of genetics for evolution in general are of the greatest importance.

The physiological fundamentals of Genetics are described under the headings *Biology* and *Cytology* and are therefore only referred to here.

The united male and female germ cells which form the beginning of each individual, contain all the genetic material which controls the future individual animal or plant. The basis of every part of the future organism is found in the two germ cells which play equal roles in their hereditary influence.

The chromosomes (*q.v.*) in the nucleus of each germ cell consist of a number of rod-shaped bodies which differ from each other and are formed from genetic material, known as genes.

The genes, themselves the heritable factors, consist of nucleoproteins and are ultra-microscopic, but each chromosome is composed of many thousands of separable genetic elements, which are visible under the microscope.

When the male and female germ cells fuse, the chromosomes pair together, each pair carrying the same genes, arranged in identical order. The fertilized egg then undergoes a cell division, known as mitosis (*q.v.*) during which all chromosomes and therefore all genes are doubled. In consequence new chromosomes are formed bearing new strings of genes, visible as split chromosomes. In the continued cell division, two daughter cells with identical number of genes as the parent cell are formed. As the nucleus of each cell of the individual contains a double set of identical chromosomes and as the egg and sperm cell contain only half that amount of chromosomes, it is

[2]From the book *A Dictionary of Science Terms* by G. E. Speck and B. Jaffee. Copyright © 1965 by Fawcett Publications. Published by Hawthorne Books, Inc., 70 Fifth Avenue, New York, New York.

evident that a reduction of chromosomes must have taken place. This reduction of meiosis (*q.v.*) occurs during the formation of the ripe egg and its objective is evident; if a chromosome reduction would not take place, the progressive accumulation of chromosomes in following generations would completely fill the cells.

Present-day genetical theory assumes that differences which develop in individuals in a uniform environment are caused by different genes. Such differences arising by a sudden change of one or more genes are called "mutations." A mutated gene continues to be propagated in its changed state until a new mutation may change it again. Organisms with such mutant genes (mutants) are used for breeding purposes. Direct genetical adaptation to environment (Lamarckism), previously believed in, has not been justified and it would now appear that inherited variations on the one side and external conditions on the other, select individuals which contain satisfactory combinations of genes.

A more frequent origin of variations than those caused by mutations, is the exchange of corresponding bits of chromosomes originating from the two parents in such a way that not all the genes of that chromosome need be transmitted. This process called "crossing-over" during the egg and sperm formation ends in a recombination of genes in the same chromosome, thus giving rise to new variations.

It has been shown that each individual has two genes for each character, derived from the male and female germ cell respectively. The individual is called "homozygous" if the two genes are alike; heterozygous, if one of the genes is a mutant gene, both then termed alleles.

In such cases the influence of one gene can be "dominant" to the other or "recessive," the latter seemingly being totally excluded. The characteristics of one parent can thus be recessive but will reappear in later generations, according to definite rules and in a definite ratio. A number of such rules of heredity were first laid down by Mendel and are recognized as Mendel's laws. See *Mendelism.* ◄

Write your notes in the space below:

1. Define genetics. _____

_____

2. Under what other headings would you find more discussion of genetics in this reference book? _____

_____

3. T or F: The united male and female germ cells which form the beginning of each individual contain all the genetic material which controls the future individual animal or plant.

4. T or F: Genes in the nucleus of each germ cell consist of a number of rod-shaped bodies called chromosomes.

5. Which contains the heritable factors?
   a. chromosomes
   b. genes
   c. nucleoproteins

6. When male and female germ cells fuse, the first step in the genetic process is
   a. cell division or mitosis.
   b. the nucleus of each cell doubles.
   c. the pairing of the chromosomes.
   d. a reduction of chromosomes.

7. Present-day genetical theory assumes that differences which develop in individuals in a uniform environment are caused by
   a. different genes.
   b. different chromosomes.
   c. different sperm cells.
   d. mitosis.

8. Lamarckism is
   a. direct genetical adaptation to environment.
   b. the term for sudden differences of one or more genes.
   c. an organism with mutant genes.
   d. not explained.

9. Each individual has
   a. two chromosomes for each characteristic.
   b. four chromosomes for each characteristic.
   c. two genes for each characteristic.
   d. four genes for each characteristic.

10. T or F: One gene can be dominant relative to the other, or recessive and not appear until later generations.

NOTES

PRACTICE **3**

Directions. Often you need to locate information quickly when doing reference work or when reviewing for a test. This exercise is a drill in using an index. Below you will find an example of an index from a psychology textbook. Using the questions which follow it as a guide, skim the index page, locate the information needed, then circle the correct response. See if you can finish in two minutes or less. Check your answers on p. 255.

► **Subject Index**[3]

L

Labyrinthine sense, 287–288

Language in thinking, 344–345

Latent content, 511

Latency period of libidinal urges, 121

Latent period, 51

Latitude of acceptance, 603

Latitude of noncommitment, 603

Latitude of rejection, 603

Law enforcement, influence on delinquency, 577

Leadership, behavior sampling for assessment, 151; characteristics of good, 566–571; responsibilities of, 562–563; styles of, 563–566; training for, 571

Leadership Evaluation and Development Scale (LEADS), 567–568

Learning, ability, 243–248; and age, 245–248; of attitudes, 189–199; characteristics of material, 225–227; criteria, 203–206; defining, 181–203; discrimination, 191–193; in emotional development, 445–448; environment and, 70; kinds of, 181–200; management of, 221–254 maturation and, 70–74; measuring, 203–209; motivation and, 221–225; motor skill learning, 197–198; neural bases of, 200–203, 666–669; part vs. whole, 236; vs. performance, 208; practice conditions conductive to, 229–239; prior, 227–229; special conditions affecting, 239–242; theories of, 214–218; verbal, 196–197

---

[3]Ruch, *op. cit.*, pp. 753–754.

227

1. What type of index is the sample?
   a. an index of terms
   b. a subject index
   c. an author index
2. Information about learning motor skills is on pages_____.
   a. 60–62
   b. 89–91
   c. 197–198
3. Information on LSD and mental illness is found on pages_____.
   a. 255–260
   b. 491–492
   c. 361–372
4. The characteristics of good leadership are found on pages _____.
   a. 566–571
   b. 466–468
   c. 22–25
5. The influence of law enforcement on delinquency is discussed on pages_____.
   a. 743–744
   b. 473–474
   c. 577
6. If you want information on the Manikin Test, turn to page_____.
   a. 366
   b. 286
   c. 160

NOTES

PRACTICE **4**

Directions. Find the page numbers for the following references listed below in the sample index page which follows them. Try to finish in less than two minutes. Check your answers on p. 255.

1. Solvated molecules, page_____
2. Solubility, on temperature, pages_____
3. Factors affecting solubility, page_____
4. Lattice defects in sodium chloride, page_____
5. "Solid alchohol," page_____
6. Standard hydrogen electrode, page_____
7. Slag, page_____
8. Solubility, table of values, page_____
9. Solo, page_____
10. Supersaturated solution, page_____

► **Index**[4]

[4]From *Chemistry*, 3rd ed., by Michell Sienko and Robert A. Plane. Copyright © 1961, 1957 by the McGraw-Hill Book Company, Inc. Used with permission of McGraw-Hill Book Company.

PRACTICE **5**

Directions. The following selection is from *Van Nostrand's Scientific Encyclopedia*, a useful reference for some types of research and term-paper assignments. Explore the passage quickly, then answer the questions which follow, ignoring the ones you can't answer. Then read closely, looking for the answers to the questions you were unable to answer. Check your answers on p. 255.

► *Leprosy*[5]

A chronic infectious disease caused by *Mycobacterium leprae.* The disease presents a great variety of signs and symptoms, depending on what tissue or organ of the body is involved.

Leprosy is a disease of antiquity, and there is evidence that it has existed at least since 2000 B.C. References to the disease are found in the Old Testament. While it has been common in the Orient for several thousands of years, it appeared as a scourge in Europe in the 11th and 12th centuries, and did not subside until the 16th century when segregation of the victims was carried out on a large scale. At present the disease occurs endemically and sporadically, chiefly in the Orient, Australia, Asia, on the Mediterranean, and in Central and South America. There are various other foci of sporadic cases such as some parts of northern and central Europe, the West Indies, Louisiana, Minnesota, and South Carolina in the United States, and several in Canada. Occasional cases are encountered in the larger seaports, both Atlantic and Pacific.

The mode of infection is not definitely known. The nasal mucosa, the gastrointestinal tract, and the skin have been considered as possible portals of entry. The disease is definitely contagious, but years of exposure and contact seem to be necessary for its transmission.

The organism causing leprosy is similar to the tubercle bacillus in appearance and staining characteristics. It is found in great numbers in the nodules occurring under the skin, in discharges from the nose and throat, and in discharges from ulcers. It was first discovered in 1873 by Hansen.

The period of incubation is variable. It may be from a few months to 20 or 30 years. The symptoms of the disease depend largely on the tissue attacked. There are two general types of the disease: (1) nodular leprosy in which the skin is primarily involved; and

[5]*Van Nostrand's Scientific Encyclopedia, op. cit.,* pp. 966–967.

(2) maculo-anaesthetic leprosy, in which there is an involvement of nervous tissue. A mixed form also occurs showing symptoms of both forms.

In the first stages of nodular leprosy, brownish-red spots appear on the skin, usually on the limbs and face, covering large and small areas of the skin. Later nodular thickenings appear at these sites. The face may show the so-called leonine appearance, due to the thickening of the skin in the region of the forehead, eyes, lobes of ears and around the nose and mouth. The entire skin assumes an unhealthy, dusky appearance. Some of the thickened areas ulcerate and fingers and toes may rot off. Ulceration also appears in the nose and throat and the voice becomes hoarse. The eyes are affected similarly, and blindness may result. This form of the disease may last 10, 20 years, or longer without treatment. Many of the patients die of complicating disorders such as pneumonia, nephritis, tuberculosis and malnutrition.

Maculo-anaesthetic leprosy is characterized by flat, red to brown lesions on the skin, distributed symmetrically. These lesions gradually become insensitive to pain (anaesthetic); trauma, even burns, may occur without the patient's feeling pain. Ulceration of the area and contractions will produce deformities.

The outlook for recovery in leprosy has been somewhat improved by modern treatment with chaulmoogra oil, or preparations derived from this oil, used either by subcutaneous or intravenous injections. A still greater advance has come with the use of derivatives of diaminodiphenylsulfone (see **Sulfonamide Drugs**) which may be given either orally or by injection and which may be expected to bring about rapid improvement especially in advanced cases and to rid the body of *mycobacterium leprae* in from two to four years. ◄

1. T or F: There is evidence that leprosy has existed for over 2000 years.
2. List where the disease occurs most often at present.
    a. _____
    b. _____
    c. _____
    d. _____
    e. _____
    f. _____
3. How is leprosy contracted?
    _____
    _____
    _____
    _____
4. The organism causing leprosy is similar to the _____
    _____

234

5. The period of incubation is variable, ranging from _____ to _____
6. Name the two types of leprosy.
   a. _____ b. _____
7. Describe the stages of nodular leprosy. _____
   _____
   _____

8. Describe the present treatment of leprosy. _____
   _____
   _____

NOTES

236

PRACTICE **6**

Directions. The following selection is a long one and enables you to put all four steps to work just as you will have to do with a regular science reading assignment. By now it should be clear to you that the four steps of this book are an integrated action rather than separate steps. However, the comprehension questions here will be broken down into the four separate steps merely so you can check to see how well you manage each step.

First, explore the following passage from a science textbook. Remember, this involves getting a general reaction to the subject matter and establishing a purpose for reading. Try to take no longer than a minute to explore. Then answer the first set of questions which follow the selection. When finished, return to the selection and check the vocabulary, analyze for comprehension, and mark the passage as you have learned. Then complete the three remaining sets of questions. Check your answers on p. 255.

▶ Mitosis[6]

Cells multiply by dividing. This arithmetic oddity means that the number of cells increases by the splitting in two of single cells. This splitting of a cell is preceded by complex events involved in the division of the nucleus, a process called *mitosis** (Figure P4.1).

When it is not reproducing, the nucleus gives little evidence of its intimate structure. It lies in the cytoplasm, revealing only its nucleolus and a fine granular appearance. Outside the nucleus in animal cells (although not in most plants) lies the centrosome, or aster, which is a star-shaped body, and at the very center of the centrosome is the minute centriole. Details of nuclear structure become abundantly apparent, however, as soon as the cell begins to reproduce.

The onset of reproductive activity is marked by the division of the aster and its centriole into two parts and the separation of these toward opposite sides of the nucleus. Within the nuclear membrane, visible changes begin as elongate threads replace the previous fine granules. These threadlike structures are the chromosomes. As we shall see, they are the carriers of the cell's inherited controls, and, consequently, the details of their structure and behavior are what we want to understand.

---

[6]Simpson and Beck, *op. cit.,* pp. 149–153.
*Strictly speaking, the division of the cell itself should be called *cytokinesis,* and the term "mitosis" should be reserved for the division of the nucleus alone. It follows that mitosis takes place only in eukaryotes (see Chapter 3). Bacteria and other prokaryotes lack nuclei and chromosomes and do not undergo mitosis.

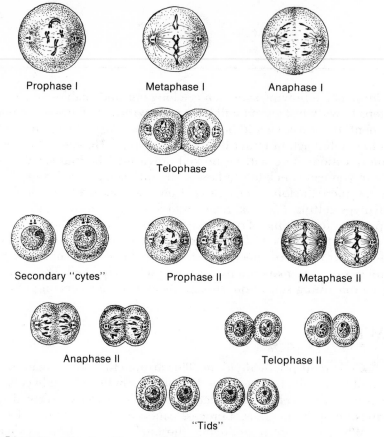

Prophase I   Metaphase I   Anaphase I

Telophase

Secondary "cytes"   Prophase II   Metaphase II

Anaphase II   Telophase II

"Tids"

Figure P4.1. The behavior of the nucleus during its mitotic cycle.

The diagrams in Figure P4.1 represent the successive events that occur during the mitotic division of a cell into two new daughter cells. The word "mitosis" derives from the Greek root *mitos* (thread) and refers to the threadlike nature of the chromosomes at mitosis. The nucleus in the figure belongs to a purely hypothetical organism in which the number of chromosomes is kept small for diagrammatic purposes. It is convenient to treat the long† and continuous process of mitosis by recognizing in it a sequence of more or less distinct stages or phases. The stages are *prophase, metaphase, anaphase,* and *telophase.*

Prophase

In prophase the chromosome threads are elongate to begin with and progressively shorten, becoming at the same time apparently

---

†The duration of mitosis varies in different cell types; it may last for minutes or for several hours.

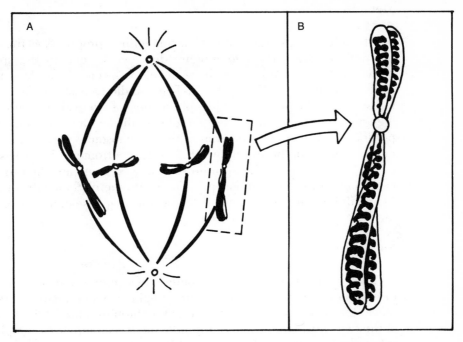

Figure P4.2. The helical structure of the metaphase chromosomes. *A*. The four chromosomes of Figure P4.1 seen on the metaphase spindle. *B*. One of the chromosomes enlarged to show how its thread is thrown into a helix and embedded in a matrix.

thicker and more heavily stainable when treated with dyes in laboratory preparations. The shortened and thickened appearance is due to the fact that the elongate thread of the earliest prophase is thrown into a helix (Figure P4.2), which sometimes becomes coated with material derived from the nucleolus. The nucleolus becomes progressively smaller during prophase.

Even from the earliest prophase, we can recognize two characteristics of the chromosomes that are fundamental and shared by almost all organisms: (1) They occur in pairs. In our hypothetical form there are two pairs (A^f and A^m, B^f and B^m). The members of each pair are similar and are said to be *homologous*. (2) Each chromosome is itself double-stranded. The two strands of each chromosome are held together by a small body called the *centromere*. Each chromosome has one centromere.

As the prophase of mitosis progresses, the two strands of each chromosome coil into helixes independently of each other; when prophase is complete, each chromosome has the appearance shown in Figure P4.1.

Metaphase

Metaphase is the stage of mitosis that follows prophase. At the end of prophase the nuclear membrane disappears,‡ and in the space between the two centrioles there develops a remarkable structure called a *spindle* (see Figure P4.1). The spindle consists of fibers that radiate from the two centrioles, producing a biconical structure. At metaphase the chromosomes migrate to the central or equatorial portion of this spindle. The arms of the chromosomes may lie loosely off the equator of the spindle itself, but the centromeres lie precisely on it. Some fibers of the spindle somehow become attached to the centromere of each chromosome. The centromeres then split in two in a definite plane (see Figure P4.1), as the anaphase of mitosis commences.

Anaphase

Each of the two daughter centromeres of a chromosome is attached to a spindle fiber. The centromeres begin to move apart. As they move, they carry with them the daughter chromosomes. Thus at each of the two ends, or poles, of the spindle there accumulates a complete set of chromosomes: A^m, A^f, B^m, and B^f.

Telophase

Telophase, which follows anaphase, is in a way the reverse of prophase. A new nuclear membrane develops around the chromosomes, which uncoil and resume their original appearance as elongate, poorly stainable threads, and the nucleolus re-forms.

Interphase

Interphase is the stage during which the nucleus is not undergoing mitosis. During interphase the chromosomes remain virtually unstainable, although we know, from a series of observations too involved to describe here, that they retain their identities as distinct bodies. ◄

---

‡The nuclear membrane, like that on the outside of the cell, owes its firmness and individuality to what is basically its gel-colloid nature. Its disappearance and later reappearance illustrate the great importance of the capacity of colloids to shift from gel to sol and back to gel. The cell can build and tear down boundary membranes where and when necessary and thus maintain order within its semifluid, semisolid state.

QUESTIONS FOR STEP

ONE

Explore

Directions. Don't guess. If you can't answer the question, leave it blank and look for the answer when you analyze for comprehension.

1. The title of this selection is _____.
2. What are the subheading titles?
   a. _____
   b. _____
   c. _____
   d. _____
   e. _____
3. What do you plan to look for as you analyze for comprehension?
   _____
   _____
   _____

Now return to the reading selection and read with Steps Two, Three, and Four in mind. Then answer the following questions.

NOTES

QUESTIONS FOR STEP

TWO

Check the Vocabulary

Directions. The following words are used in the selection you just read. Select the best definition for each word.

1. *mitosis*
   a. cell division
   b. the splitting in two of a single cell
   c. cell multiplication
2. *cytoplasm*
   a. the nucleus of a cell
   b. the star-shaped body in the center of the cell
   c. the protoplasm of a cell, excluding the nucleus
3. *elongate*
   a. short
   b. narrow
   c. long and narrow
4. *hypothetical*
   a. imaginary
   b. real
   c. fundamental
5. *interphase*
   a. stage of mitosis
   b. stage in which the nucleus is not undergoing mitosis
   c. center stage of mitosis
6. *metaphase*
   a. first major stage of mitosis
   b. second major stage of mitosis
   c. third major stage of mitosis
7. *anaphase*
   a. second major stage of mitosis
   b. third major stage of mitosis
   c. fourth major stage of mitosis

8. *telophase*
   a. second major stage of mitosis
   b. third major stage of mitosis
   c. fourth major stage of mitosis
9. *centromere*
   a. a small body holding two strands of chromosomes together
   b. center of a chromosome
   c. the space between two centrioles
10. *biconical*
   a. resembling a cone
   b. resembling two cones
   c. resembling three cones

QUESTIONS FOR STEP

THREE

Analyze for Comprehension

Directions. Answer the following questions without referring back to the article.

1. The splitting of a cell is preceded by complex events involved in the division of the _____.
2. The nucleus of a cell lies in the _____.
3. The word "mitosis" is derived from the Greek root *mitos* and refers to _____ _____.

4. Even in the earliest stage, prophase, two characteristics of the chromosomes are shared by almost all organisms
   (a) _____and
   (b) _____.
5. The correct order of stages in mitosis is as follows:
   (a) _____
   (b) _____
   (c) _____
   (d) _____
   (e) _____
6. T or F: Metaphase is characterized by the chromosomes migrating to the central or equatorial portion of a structure called the spindle.
7. T or F: Anaphase is characterized by the centromeres moving apart.
8. T or F: Telophase is characterized by a new nuclear membrane developing around the chromosomes, which then uncoil and resume their original appearance.
9. T or F: Interphase is the stage during which the nucleus is not undergoing mitosis.
10. Explain how the nuclear membrane can disappear and later reappear. _____ _____ _____

NOTES

FOUR

Synthesize for Understanding

Directions. These questions require you to make personal connections with what you have read. Since responses will vary, there are no answers in the key. You will have to judge the validity of your responses.

1. Of what importance is mitosis to you?

   _____
   _____
   _____
   _____

2. What did you learn about mitosis that you did not know before reading this selection?

   _____
   _____
   _____
   _____

3. How much do you feel that the application of the four steps used here can help you with your science reading assignments?

   _____
   _____
   _____
   _____

4. How earnestly have you applied the skills learned in this book to the last drill? To your science reading assignments?

   _____
   _____
   _____
   _____

Answer Key

STEP

ONE
Explore

Practice **1**
1. three
2. F
3. T
4. the fossil record
5. d

Practice **2**
1. d
2. a
3. F
4. F
5. d
6. T

Practice **3**
1. ability to learn
2. b
3. T
4. T
5. You could have listed the four subheadings or you could have listed any four questions you personally want answers to.

Practice **4**
1. all but d and h
2. dissecting needles, methyl green, pencil and paper for sketching
3. b
4. F

Practice **5**
1. c
2. b
3. a
4. b
5. b

TWO

Check the Vocabulary

Practice **1**
1. b
2. a
3. c
4. b

Practice **2**
1. b
2. b
3. a
4. c

Practice **3**
1. a person who fits hearing aids for the hard-of-hearing
2. spontaneous generation; self-generating
3. destroying bacteria
4. inflammation of the joints
5. studying of mankind and its evolution
6. branch of chemistry that deals with the life processes of plants and animals
7. of the heart
8. a mollusk having a head and two large eyes and tentacles, such as an octopus
9. green coloring matter of plants
10. instrument for measuring time
11. study of cells
12. measurement across
13. outer skin
14. study of origins or heredity
15. science that deals with the effects of weather, winds on the earth
16. uncontrollable bleeding

17. instrument for measuring water
18. the universe
19. an instrument for measuring small distances and angles
20. study of the nervous system
21. eight-angled shape
22. dealing with ailments by treating displaced bones or nerves
23. fear of man
24. many angles
25. study of animals

Practice 4
1. a tank for keeping water animals alive
2. the science dealing with hearing
3. a graph showing hearing loss
4. received through the ear
5. a plant that eats insects
6. fleshy, fat body
7. having separate fingers or toes or divisions
8. inactive
9. waterway
10. helpful
11. a seed plant that grows by adding layers on the outside
12. place or area close by
13. instrument for sending signals
14. a place where corpses are prepared for burial
15. eventually must die
16. an ophthalmologist
17. an instrument that measures distances walked
18. easily carried
19. examination of dead body
20. predict before it happens
21. to forecast or predict cause of illness
22. ruddy; the color of blood
23. sleepwalker
24. having to do with the sun
25. a magnetic tape used for filming TV programs for later use

Practice 5
1. treatment of disease by means of substances such as penicillin, vaccines, and the like
2. Greek
3. *bio* = life; *therapy* = treatment
4. a motion-picture projector
5. an examination to determine whether life is present
6. *bi* = two; *bio* = life

7. ecology
8. law
9. the science dealing with the natural principles controlling the life process
10. extremely important

STEP

THREE

Analyze for Comprehension

Practice **1**
1. kinds of frustration
2. environmental, personal, and conflict frustrations
3.

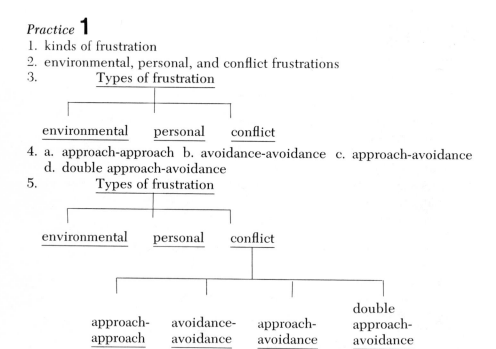

Types of frustration

environmental   personal   conflict

4. a. approach-approach b. avoidance-avoidance c. approach-avoidance
   d. double approach-avoidance
5.

Types of frustration

environmental   personal   conflict

approach-   avoidance-   approach-   double
approach   avoidance   avoidance   approach-
                                        avoidance

Practice **2**
1. the process of bone growth

252

2. two ways: length and width. The growth in length is done near the end of the bone. The growth in width is done by nonbony sheaths encircling the outside of the bone.
3. Since bone is added on the outside and the inner bone cells digest the bone on the inner walls, room is made for the soft marrow. In this case, the ring is eventually "free" in the marrow.
4. *peri* = around; *osteon* = bone, or around the bone
5. a thin nonbony sheath that encircles the bone and lays down new bone on the outside

Practice 3
1. c
2. (a) turning liquid to a firm solid; clotting
   (b) a disease in which blood clots too slowly to prevent death
   (c) too much clotting of the blood, forming a plug and stopping the blood flow
   (d) a term which describes blood clots being carried around in the blood stream and lodging in a vessel
3. (a) blood
   (b) loving
   (c) thicken
   (d) too much
   (e) plug
4. c

Practice 4
1. c
2. A ring is cut into the bark around the stem or a branch of a tree so that the externally located phloem is cut but the xylem is not. Organic materials accumulate above the ring, showing a downward path has been interrupted.
3. The leaves above the cut wilt, showing water is not traveling upward from the roots.
4. Malpighi, an Italian biologist in the seventeenth century
5. the use of radioactive labeling of photosynthetic products with $C_{14}O_2$

Practice 5
1. the four fundamental forms of measurement
2. length, mass, time, and electric current
3. the British system and the metric system
4. a
5.

The British system	The Metric system
(a) foot	(a) meter
(b) slug	(b) kilogram
(c) second	(c) second
(d) ampere	(d) ampere

Practice **6**

1. d
2. a
3. fruit fly
4. led the way to understanding how certain hereditary traits are transferred

Practice **7**

1. b
2. c
3. b
4. because they promote rapid chemical change which otherwise would proceed too slowly

STEP

FOUR

Synthesize for Understanding

Practice **1**

1. a moving mass of ice, partially melting and slowly moving downhill
2. Deposits of nonmelting snow accumulate from year to year; partial melting and increase in pressure cause the lower level to change to ice.
3. Valley glaciers are patches and tongues of dirty ice lying in mountain valleys, and move slowly; ice caps are huge masses of ice engulfing hills and valleys, and move rapidly.

Practice **2**

1. the science concerned with the study of the inborn properties and differences which determine heredity
2. biology, cytology, and Mendelism

3. T	7. a
4. F	8. a
5. b	9. c
6. c	10. T

254

Practice **3**
1. b
2. c
3. b
4. a
5. c
6. c

Practice **4**
1. 216
2. 223–225
3. 222–226
4. 188
5. 247
6. 310
7. 440
8. 406, 625, 626
9. 246
10. 226

Practice **5**
1. T
2. (a) Orient; (b) Australia; (c) Asia; (d) Mediterranean; (e) Central America; (f) South America
3. It is not definitely known, but years of exposure and contact seem necessary for transmission.
4. tubercle bacillus
5. a few months to 20 to 30 years
6. (a) nodular (skin) and (b) maculo-anaesthetic leprosy (nervous tissue)
7. See paragraph 6 for comparison purposes
8. chaulmoogra oil and derivatives of sulfonamide drugs by oral means or injections

Step One
1. mitosis
2. (a) prophase; (b) metaphase; (c) anaphase; (d) telophase; (e) interphase (a and e can be reversed)
3. Answers will vary.

Step Two
1. b
2. c
3. c
4. a
5. b
6. b
7. b
8. c
9. a
10. b

Step Three

1. nucleus
2. cytoplasm
3. the threadlike nature of the chromosomes at mitosis
4. (a) Chromosomes occur in pairs and (b) each chromosome is double-
   stranded.
5. (a) prophase (b) metaphase (c) anaphase (d) telophase (e) interphase
6. T
7. T
8. T
9. T
10. See footnote ‡ in the reading selection and compare your answer.

Step Four

Answers will vary.

DATE DUE

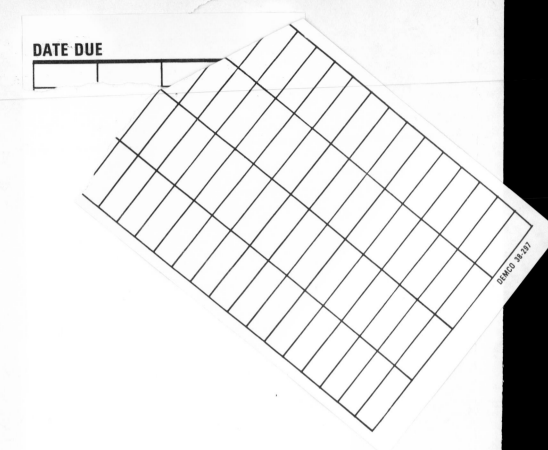

DEMCO 38-297

1 2 3 4 5 6 7 8 9 10 11 12 13 14 15   75 74 73 72 71 70 69